ARABIC NUMERALS

A. S. Shakiry

ARABIC NUMERALS

AUTHOR

A. S. Shakiry

PUBLISHER

T.C.P.H. Ltd

(technical consulting and publishing house)

Established in 1982

www.islamictourism.com
www.iraqicharities.org
shakiry@tcph.org

U.K. REGISTRATION
Nº 1645411

Table of Contents

Stages (Periods) in Shakiry's Life

1931   Born in Iraq and grew up in the Holy City of Najaf, attending the traditional religious schools.

1942   He start his practical life under the auspices of his brother Jawad al-Shakiry and during that time he continued to educate himself.

1947-1948   Settled in Lebanon for twenty months, that created opportunities and Prospects for his life.

1949   Entered Business & the Industry worlds, he established Dijla Shoe Mfg Company with his brothers Jawad and Hussain al-Shakiry.

1955   Travelled to Germany to participate in a special training course on the chemistry and technology of rubber; he also participated in some of the European specialized exhibitions.

1958   Participated in a course in Svit Factories for Shoe and Rubber Manufacturing (Formerly named Bata) in Czechoslovakia; he travelled from there to Germany, France & Italy.

1959   Stayed in Frankfurt for ten months, he had enlisted himself on different courses on production management, cost calculation of hourly productivity and computer systems using the giant IBM, then he joined Berlet School in Frankfurt to learn the German language.

1962   He took part in a higher management study course in Baghdad, under the supervision of Dr. Hassan Salman, Head of the Industrial Development Department.

1963-1964   He bought DAMA GmbH Company in Germany which he ran, the company specialized in marketing and servicing "Maytag", American washing machines that used coins which was new to Europe.

1965   Attended & participated in the conference of the International Labour Organization (ILO) in Geneva.

1966   Established a new company called Rafid Shoe Mfg Co WLL. He also inaugurated twenty branches for selling their products, then he founded three more companies:
- Aldhia'a Polymers Product Mfg. Co WLL for Glues and Varnishes.
- United Polymers Products Co WLL.
- At-Timsah Straps & Belts Mfg Co. WLL.
The number of the workers and staff exceeded 600.

1980   Moved to United Kingdom & settled until the present.

Stages (Periods) in Shakiry's Life

1983 He established a company called T.C.P.H Ltd for Publishing & Distribution which issued:
- AlHidhaa international magazine, for Leather & Shoes.
- Alridaa international magazine, for Textile and Clothing.
He Founded Rafid shoe Ltd.
He managed to register a patent in the method of fast shoe making (instant made to measure shoes).

1986 Entered a partnership with a biscuit company in Morocco, and then he became the sole owner of it.

1999 Publish his first book "Financial Worship in Islam"

2001 He issued the third magazine, a specialized magazine named Islamic Tourism magazine, which is still issued in five languages (Arabic, English, French, Spanish and German), and their websites: www.islamictourism.com

2002 Published his second book entitled "The Humanitarian Jihad in Islam"

2005 Established al-Shakiry Charity for Social Interdependence in Iraq which cares for more than 600 orphans.

He also Established Iraqi Charities Forum which includes tens of registered charities inside and outside Iraq, and the website: www. iraqicharities.org

2007 - Published his third book Tourism Prospects which included all his articles in Islamic tourism magazines until issue 27.
- Until 2008, he continues to supply the magazine with articles called 'Tourism prospects' for each issue.
- Also he enriched the Iraqi Charities Forum website with his weekly letters which handled different subjects, from articles of academic base to set up, manage and run charities and finally how to promote the philanthropy and giving culture.
- Participated in a lot of discussion in academic and scientific conferences as well as in a variety of exhibitions.

2008 - Published his fourth book: Islamic Tourism Prospects for World Peace, in Arabic.
- Published his fourth book: Islamic Tourism Prospects for World Peace, in English.

❖ He is due to publish one book: Industrial Horizons.

Dedication

Our Arabic Numbers in the Arena of Civilizations

No two people disagree over stressing the fact that civilization grew out of Mesopotamia and the surrounding expanses of land. Mankind found its developed and multifaceted status, with its urban and social entities, around the area known today as the Arabian Peninsula and Mesopotamia. From this noble land emanated the Muhammadan light to illuminate the regions of the world with its glow, knowledge and a permanence that is reminiscent of the permanence of solar eternity, reckoning and judgment. There is no doubt that a race, which gives rise to a civilization from which a number of civilizations originate, must possess both a communicative language and a descriptive language in order to exist. Therefore, the numerical language was, in our own estimation, the first language used by mankind because it describes and embodies things. Moreover, the human body has so many parts that are amenable to being counted, such as fingers, ribs, legs and other bodily parts, as to set the stage for ascertaining and learning the numerical language in order to describe things in terms of their numbers rather than essence. That furnishes us with the conclusion that numbers enjoy the greatest potential for survival, evolution and openness toward knowledge, the sciences, and continued existence till the Day of Judgment. Even the universe, in which we exist, with all the moons and suns that it contains, is described by Allah as "following a reckoning".

Even in the descriptions given by the One and Only Creator to existence, life, death and monotheism, we observe numbers with overlapping vigour when they denote computational descriptions and evaluative descriptions. When Allah addresses Adam and Eve in His Noble Book, He addresses them using a numerical language. And when He asks the angels to provide the names of the new creation, He addresses them using a numerical description. We do not engage in allegorical hyperbole when we say that He addresses them at the beginning of creation with a numerical description and in Arabic since the Noble Prophet of the Ummah has said: "I am fond of the Arabs for three reasons: because I am an Arab, and because the Qur'an is in Arabic, and because Arabic is the language of the inhabitants of Paradise". In other words, addressing Adam and Eve in Arabic involved the descriptive capacity of numbers " but do not go near this tree," The Elevated Places 19. That is also the case when He addresses Satan ("Lo! thou art of those reprieved") "He said:

Surely you are of the respited ones." The Elevated Places 15; and when He addresses the angels, they reply ("we have no knowledge but that which Thou hast taught us") "They said: Glory be to Thee! we have no knowledge, but that which Thou hast taught us; surely Thou art the knowing, the wise." The Cow 32; and when He describes the Heavens and the earth, He describes them using descriptive numbers. However, when He talks about the existence and the universe He pinpoints six days; that is using an existential number.

The purpose of this cursory sketch is to say that the rhetorical character of the Arabic language consists of a numerical descriptive idiom that sets it apart in essence from all other languages, modern and past ones. You do not find singular, dual, and plural forms except in the Arabic language. All other languages use only the singular and the plural forms. Therefore, as creation started in this region, which we identified above, it found, before it set up the city-state and the state and the appearance of Sargon the Akkadian who united the region and founded the first empire in history, that numbers constitute the real language that should dominate. Perhaps civilizations and the precious things that they left at the Louvre Museum in France provide the best evidence of that. By merely looking at a piece left over from the Mesopotamian civilization we find that it bears inscriptions and that numbers figure as mainstays of these inscriptions; whereas one rarely finds writings or numbers on the precious items of other, posterior civilizations. Consequently, the numerical language is not a modern legacy, but rather a legacy that dates back to the beginning of the Godly creation. Allah has taught this Godly legacy to His creation so that they would discover through this legacy other things that would consolidate their presence on, and connection with, the earth and with life. At the beginning of creation, when a man possesses money, land or beasts, his description of his possessions was numerical in terms of their numbers and in the way that he deemed appropriate at the time. In addition, throughout the descriptive composition of its verses, the Noble Book is replete with numbers, especially when we set out in company with the Noble Book to delve into the rumbling depths of the unseen and the successive nations as well as to identify the properties of judgment, punishment, good deeds and wrongdoing.

Talking about numbers in this manner is intended to identify the civilizations that dealt with numbers and turned them into a reality that can be attributed to them, thus countering an obscurity borne out of the passage of time. This leads us to the conclusion that the West and some parts of the East were not at the beginning of civilizations concerned with numbers. Rather, whatever they passed on (with respect to numbers) was inherited from other civilizations which infiltrated them through expansion or recurring wars. As such, India and the West did not exist at the beginning of

Dedication

creation. Human existence with all its aspects was at the beginning of creation restricted to the area between the Arabian Peninsula and Mesopotamia as well as along the banks of the two rivers (the Euphrates and the Tigris) whose geographic scope extended at the time to Egypt to the west, and northwards to what is nowadays modern Turkey and some parts of Greece where Greek civilization grew. Consequently, if archeological research is to plumb the depths of this question and subject matter, it will find that Greek civilization is an acquired civilization and not a developed legacy like the civilizations that were born in the regions that we have identified earlier. This leads us to a conclusion professing that the findings of Mr Abdul Sahib al-Shakiry in his book entitled "Our Arabic Numbers" are correct, accurate and beyond a shadow of a doubt.

There is no doubt that "Our Arabic Numbers," which I consider to be a valuable work, will be an important work in both the near and distant future. It portrayed, beautifully, in an accessible linguistic context, and by using valuable investigative proofs, the scientific evolution which accompanied the path of Arabs and Muslims. The scientific content of the first two chapters, which touched on Arabian achievements in mathematics and the effect of numbers on other sciences, was perhaps a notion that is necessary for Arab and Muslim researchers, especially at a time that is replete with following in the footsteps of all that which is Western, and rejecting all that which is Arab and Islamic. A malcontent might raise an objection to us, saying: "What is the use of the past and talking about it?" In fact, nations that have no history can never rise up and remain mired in backwardness. Conceivably, no scientific research can develop without referring to the historical foundations of sciences. This clear and modest narrative, expounded by Mr Shakiry opened up before us many vistas for proving the Arab and Islamic origins of numbers and the developed and progressive status of the Arabs and Muslims at the time, whereas other nations were completely mired in backwardness. The greater advantage that I found in the author's discourse, and which is rightly considered a new numerical philosophy, lies in his discussion of the role of the Abbasid state in the growth of sciences, especially in inventing the clock. When mathematicians fixed the divisions of the clock at the time, they took into account that time starts from zero and, in the light of this, time was divided into hours, minutes and seconds. Perhaps, this scientific breakthrough in mathematics, which was preceded by a breakthrough in the field of numbers and their uses, paved the way for the emergence of many sciences that had a momentous impact on the development of other sciences.

The fact is that Arabic is a numerical, mathematical language. The prosodic scales of classical Arabic poetry are indeed an example of this fact, if we take into consideration that these scales of classical Arabic poetry depend on movement and stasis, known nowadays as binary numbers composed of 0 and 1. Accordingly, and irrespective of the existence of multiple theories, we tend towards the opinion of the researcher, Mr. Shakiry, that the zero is of Arab origin and was derived from language before its uses effected a change in the concepts of engineering, physics, chemistry, and other sciences, whether those sciences in which the Arabs and Muslims showed creativity or those in which they never showed any creativity. The findings of Mr. Abdul Sahib al-Shakiry are not a matter of contention among researchers. As they persist in verifying their thesis, even the proponents of the Indian (origin of the) zero finally stand bewildered at a crossroads: they say that there are also theories that prove the Arab origins of the zero which were passed on (to Europe) through the Arab state in Andalusia. Some go beyond that and say that the zero entered with the Fatimid occupation of Central Europe.

The researcher, Mr. Abdul Sahib al-Shakiry has roamed the terrain of the writing of letters and how to deal with them, from the standpoint of the Chinese, Phoenician, Indian, Western, Eastern and other languages which have civilizations. These civilizations played a role in firming up and developing sciences despite the fact that most of them were borrowed and non-inherited, as we have described them. Accordingly, al-Shakiry was able, in a competent mathematical investigative spirit, to explain the forms and circumstances within which numbers came into being, and the particulars of writing their forms. In his findings, he arrived at the Arab origins of numbers, and this is a purely logical, mathematical conclusion that should be resorted to in any research in this field. Through this finding, he linked the importance of growth in the modern sciences to numbers, and the impact of this growth on the manner in which an Arab scientific system can be built. This system facilitates entering the stage of scientific development by means of numbers and their computerized processing. This opinion is on the mark and it is necessary to set out to understand this reality.

The call made by the researcher with respect to the importance of the use of the Arabic numbers (0; 1; 2; 3; etc) is a genuine call that is clearly concerned with the development of the sciences and their contributions. This is something that, as the researcher says, can only be achieved if they were adopted by all Arab and Islamic states so as to put the record straight and that we act to develop and verify it. This will be an opportunity to redeem and make amends for the illustrious scientific Arab and Islamic names, such as Khawarizmi, Bayruni and others, whose heritage was stolen and was attributed to names that would have had no role or meaning had it not been for their theft of the rights of those (Arab and Islamic scientists).

Dedication

It is not surprising that this research comes from our Brother Mr. Abdul Sahib al-Shakiry because he had previously supplied the Arab library with research works and magazines dealing with topics that no one else before him had paid attention to. I especially would like to mention the al-Hidha' ('The Shoe') magazine, the al-Rida' ('The Attire') magazine, and Islamic Tourism magazine ('ITM'). Without him, the Western reader would have never had a chance to get to know the contributions of the Arabs and Muslims (in these fields); as he was extremely keen to publish these publications in both Arabic and English. Moreover, he has since been persistent in publishing his output in English and other modern European languages, in addition to Arabic, so that Western society would be able to find out about the research output of Arabs and Muslims. May Allah bless you. I will be awaiting further works.

Dr. Haitham Ghalib al-Nahi
London
21 December 2008

Introduction

My questions about and interests in Arabic Numerals have been growing daily since the beginning of the 1980s, when I was publishing the magazines 'Al Hithaa' (Shoes), and 'Ar Ridaa' (Clothes), which were published bilingually in English and Arabic. And because the two magazines were focussed on professional, scientific and economic affairs, since they were both professional magazines, such scientific issues would naturally require tables and numbers. With every issue of the two magazines, I used to feel upset and grieved as I didn't feel there was a need or justification to use two kinds of numbers, especially when both sets of numbers are considered to be Arabic. In addition, the Oriental numerals are difficult to read or write and the possibility of making mistakes in their usage is greater than others. For this reason, I thought using two types of numbers was both time-consuming and effort-wasting, as well as impeding artistic, scientific and discourse excellence. There are also many justifications in design, presentation and others which give our Arabic numerals many advantages over their oriental rivals.

Over the years, my desire and tendency towards using our Arabic numerals has increased. Arabic numerals, which are Arabic in origin but western and international by usage, are used in Arabic North African countries and most countries of the world, and they are even called Arabic Numerals. On the other hand, the other oriental numerals are Indian by origin. (For simplicity, I am going to use the term 'our Arabic Numerals' for what is widely known as 'Arabic Numerals' while referring to the other set of numbers as 'Oriental Numerals'.

After this, I began to insist on using the term 'our Arabic Numerals' and encourage workers who were working on publishing the two magazines to use them. When we bought our computers, I requested staff to use our Arabic Numerals instead of Oriental Numerals, but the software of our computers then accepted only Oriental Numerals. The transformation into Arabic Numerals was a complex issue that would have taken a long time as every number had to be changed manually and the result could be a mixture of the two types of numerals in Arabic texts. The urge to change the numerals remained with me every time I was engaged in editing or publishing a book or a magazine.

When I published my book, 'Financial Worships in Islam', my insistence was clear on the need to achieve what I believe to be right, that is writing all the numbers in the book, even the numbers of the Quraanic verses, in Arabic

Numerals. I was in Morocco at the time, and it was obvious to me that the future was for our Arabic Numerals.

Here I am again attempting to publish this book after a delay of a number of years due to my other engagements with publishing the Islamic Tourism Magazine and establishing a website for it.

The idea of writing a book about Arabic Numerals has been brewing since the early nineties, and ever since I have been looking for sources that might help me to achieve this study. I had to subscribe to the British National Library which is the biggest advanced library in London and I started talking with friends about the subject of this book. Then I was reunited with a childhood friend Mr Abdul Lateef Al Milih, the former member of the Baghdadi Heritage Association, who died before achieving his wish to see this book published. May God bless his soul. I spoke to him about the Arabic Numerals and he said he would search the shelves of Iraqi libraries for sources and 'there must be some answers for all your questions' and how the numerals developed, where they came from and how. He kept his promise and supplied me with a valuable study which I will quote in this book – a study that has really become an important pillar in this book. A thousand thanks to Abdul Lateef Al Milih for his valuable contribution to this book.

Now, after all the elements of this book were completed, such as historical research, justifications for change, technological and scientific basics, and after giving examples of other nations' experiences and their leaderships into revolutionary changes in scientific, and cultural fields as well as reconstruction and all that is related to the development of human beings and humanity, we must call upon all governments of our Arab countries, whose media and cultural establishments are still in two minds between Oriental Numerals and our Arabic Numerals which has now been accepted by 95% of countries of the world. We say to them that the time is now right for taking quick revolutionary but scientific steps in order to change the numbers in educational syllabi as well as in media and publishing. This way we will conform to countries of the world and the requirements of modern technology within the computer and communication revolution…

It is time for Arab countries to initiate a change and unify numbers across our Arab nation. This can be done through calling for the replacement of Oriental Numerals with our Arabic Numerals in all Arab countries which still use Oriental Numerals. They, our Arabic Numerals, are both original and internationally used. This must be executed in a scientific and organized way as was the case with the European Union when it unified the currencies of 25

Introduction

countries and introduced a single currency for all of them, the Euro. Is reclaiming what was taken from us, which is the numerals that are called after our name, Arabic numerals, and putting them in place of Oriental Numerals, which no longer conform to modern technology and science, an impossible task to implement? Is it really that complex or difficult a task? The answer is definitely NO. It is an easy task, in fact very easy after all the required programmes and software have been developed and modern computers can now handle them with no difficulty. Computer operators can now press a button and all numbers can change within the Arabic text or all other texts printed on the computer, from one type to another, no matter what shapes or types they take. Let us embark into the study of this book, (Arabic Numerals)…

At the end of my introduction, this, I find it a must for me to put my thanks and gratitude to all people who helped me in the research, review and classification of the texts of this book and its translation. Besides, my thanks to all brothers and sisters who participated in the typesetting, printing and accomplishing of this work.

God is the ultimate guarantor of success.

A. S. Shakiry

Chapter One

Mathematics during the times
of Arab Muslims

Mathematics

It is a well-known fact that Arab Muslims based their knowledge of mathematics on the sciences they received from the Greeks and the Indians. But they also developed these sciences and advanced them many steps forward, until many distinguished scientists in mathematics appeared in the Orient such as Al Khawarizmi (born AD 844), Thabit Bin Qurra (born AD 901), Al Bettani (born AD 926), Al Khazin Al Basri (born circa AD 960), and Omar Bin Ibrahim Al Khayyam (born AD 1132). Also, in the Islamic West (North Africa), there was Muslima Al Majreeti (born AD 1007) who was nicknamed the 'Imam of mathematicians in the Arab Andalus' (Andalusia in Spain where the Moors ruled). Many of his students also became famous mathematicians such as Ibn As-Samh (born AD 1034), Ibn As-Saffar, Al Karamani and others.

The Muslims advanced arithmetic by huge steps, as they added to the Greeks' information a great deal of theories which Europe didn't previously know. They also taught the Europeans the system of Indian numerals, which represented a comprehensive revolution in the science of arithmetic. It is clear to us that this numerical system has facilitated arithmetic and accounting transactions if we are to compare it to the Roman numerical system. Within the new numerical system which Europe acquired from the Arabs, the value of number '1' for example, changes depending on its position in the figure, whether it is in the decimal, units, tenth, hundredth, thousandth or the millionth mathematical position. However, the value of the number in the Roman numeric system doesn't change when its mathematical position changes. The number '5', for example, remains as 'five' (in value) and cannot mean '50' or '500', or '5000'. The same goes if we want to write the number '27' in the Latin Numerals, which Europe used in the Middle Ages and knew no other numerals. It will be written as follows: XXV11. We can imagine the extent of complication this adds to the accounting and mathematical process such as addition, subtraction, division and multiplication if we use the Roman numerical system, let alone if we use it for large figures expressed in thousands and millions.

The new numerals used in the West are not a western invention. It is likely that it was Indian as the Arabs indicated, and as it is clear from the way they are written, from left to right. The credit goes to the Arabs who introduced this new system to Europe and relieved the Europeans of the complications of the old Roman numerical system. They facilitated the accounting and arithmetic process and helped the science of mathematics to progress.

Al Bairooni wrote an important book about numbers and their ratios – he called it *'Rashikat Al Hind'* or 'Indian Numerals'. Al Ya'aqoobi also explained

Chapter 1

in his book 'The History' the new numerical system which the Arabs learned from the Indians. He said: "...They put nine Indian digits, of which all arithmetic operations are derived from, but without fully knowing what they represent. These are '1, 2, 3, 4, 5, 6, 7, 8, 9)...' The first set was 'one, ten, and a hundred'. They also represent one thousand, one hundred thousand and one thousand thousand.... On this method of calculation, the nine digits also work upwards. The category of 'one', for example, is distinct from the 'ten', and the category of ten is distinct from the hundred, and so on for every category. If any category doesn't have a digit, a 'zero' should be in its place. The 'zero' should be a circle shape '0'".

We can see from the above that Al Ya'aqoobi refers to a new arithmetic symbol which is 'zero' which is one of the most important principles in mathematics that the human mind has discovered. The West didn't know the usage of the 'zero' until the Arabs introduced it in the 12th century A.D. Even the historian *Eyre* said that the idea of 'zero' was one of the great gifts that the Muslims have given to Western Europe. The Arabs used the word 'zero' (meaning *zephirum* in Latin or Sifr in Arabic), to refer to 'nothing', since the *Jahili* era ('*jahili*' is an Arabic word derived form the root 'jahal' which means 'ignorance' in Arabic, and hence the phrase literally means 'the era of ignorance' which is the period that preceded Islam. It's a term coined by the Prophet Muhammed). The following verse which came within a whole poem by the Arab poet Hatim Al Taei has the word 'zero' in it.

ترى إن ما أهلكتُ لم يكُ ضرني   وإن يديَّ مما بخلتُ به صفرُ

Meaning: Inevitably, I will leave this world. It will be clear then, that what I had spent had been of no harm to me, while my hands would be empty of what I had striven hard to save (the poet literally used the word 'zero' in the sentence 'my hands will have zero money on them of the money I was so careful not to spend'), which actually means: (I would get no benefit from saving money).

During the 8th century A.D. the Muslims used 'zero' in arithmetic and they drew it in a circle shape as *Ya'aqoobi* mentioned previously.

Muhammed Bin Ahmed also mentioned in his book (*Mafateeh ul Uloom or 'The Keys of Sciences'*), that if there is no number indicated in the arithmetic process, we should use a 'small circle' in order to make the set of numbers even. Al Khawarizmi also explained how to use the new numbers, including zero, in a study that was translated by the Europeans into Latin in the first quarter of the 12th century A.D. under the name: '*Algoritmi de Numero Indorum*' which translates as 'Al Khawarizmi on Indian Numerals'. This means the European word *'Chiffre'* was derived from the Arabic Sifr = zero, and it also means 'nothing or valueless'. Martin Luther used this word to describe the weakness of the bishops in front of the Pope. He described them as 'zeros'… In the 16th century A.D. the European expression 'chiffre' or 'code' was used to signify vague writing, while the word 'zero' was used to mean 'nothing'…

Western Europe received the new numerical system that is associated with Al Khawarizmi's name which had soon been adjusted in Latin to 'Algoritmi' then Algorismus then abbreviated to Augurim. The latter expression became the name of a new science which is the new decimal numbers. This shows that westerners have actually learned modern arithmetic from the former Al Khawarizmi book and other books derived from his book such as *Carmen de Algorisme*, written by *Alexandre De Villa* and Algorismus Vulgaris by John of Halifax in AD 1250. Both of these books were based on the book of Muhammed Bin Musa Al Khawarizmi in arithmetic and both of them remained authoritative referral sources for learning arithmetic in Western Europe for centuries.

The word Algorithm, derived from AL Khawarizmi's name, is still used in the English language today to refer to the given method of problem solving.

The Arab's service to Europe is not limited to arithmetic in the sphere of mathematics, but it extended to other sciences, at the top of which was Algebra, which has kept its Arabic name in all European languages (Algebra or Algebre), after the Europeans learned it from the Arabs. If some researchers tend to believe that Arabs were not those who laid the bases for the science of Algebra, and if they think that the rules of the science were known since the days of *Diophantus*, a Greek scientist who lived in the third century A.D., it is sufficient pride for the Arabs to have established the origins of Algebra science and made advances in it and transformed it completely. They have turned it into a real and complete science. They then applied it to engineering. The Arabs were so dedicated to algebra that the caliph Al Ma'amoon commissioned Muhammed Bin Musa Al Khawarizmi to write a book on this science. It's the book that was translated into Latin by *Robert of Chester* in the year AD 1145. By this achievement, the Arabs had presented Europe with a new science as this book remained in use in European schools and universities until the 16th century A.D.

One of the Arab scientists who worked and wrote in Algebra was *Abu Bakir Muhammed Bin Al Karkhi* who died circa AD 1019-1020. Ibn Al Karkhis is regarded as one of the most senior scientists that Baghdad witnessed in the era of *Abi Ghalib Muhammed Bin Khalaf,* who was nicknamed 'Fakhr ul Mulk' or The Pride of the Crown and who was a minister during the era of *Baha uddeen Idhd*

Chapter 1

Ad Dawla Bin Buwayh. Al Karkhi wrote two books "Al Fakhri Fi Algebr Wa Al Muqabela" or The Pride in Algebra and Comparison and "Al Kafi Fil Hisab" or The Sufficient in Arithmetic. The first book is more important, and it comes second in importance to the book written in the science of Algebra by Omar Bin Ibrahim Al Khayyam (AD 1045-1123).

As for geometry and trigonometry, the Arabs translated the book of Euclides in geometry and it is the same translation that the European used to translate into Latin in the 12th century A.D. Also, Al Koosi translated the book of Al Mu'atayat or The Elements by Euclides. It is a book that deals with the geometry of the globular shapes in the year AD 1274. The Arabs didn't just limit their books to the knowledge they inherited from the Greeks in geometry and trigonometry, but they renewed it and included new valuable additions which were not known before them. They were the first to introduce *the tangent* into the science of trigonometry calculation. This step was very important in mathematics and it was regarded by mathematical scientists as a serious scientific revolution. The Arabs used sines and *cosines* in place of *hypotenuse*, and solved cubic equations. They also progressed deeply into the studies of the *cones*. All this new information was no doubt instrumental in making mathematical sciences have such an important role in life.

Among the most prominent Arab Muslim scientists who worked and wrote in geometry, trigonometry and calculus were Al Khawarizmi, Thabit Bin Qurra, Al Battani, Al Khazin Al Basri, Ibn AL Haytham, and Al Bairooni. Abu Abdulla Al Battani (AD 850-939), who is known among Europeans as Albategnus, advanced the science of trigonometry calculus to a great extent, and further than it was during the days of Euclid of Alexandria. He replaced triangles with squares in equation solving and the angle sine by the arc. He was also the scientist who originated the science of trigonometric calculation by ratio in the way that is in use today. As for Ibn Al Haytham's essay in trigonometry calculus, it is called 'The shape of Beni Musa'. He explains the reason for naming it like this by saying 'The shapes that Beni Musa' introduced using the proofs found in the book of Cones by Polonius, the famous Greek astrologist and mathematician, was the last shape in their introductions. As for Al Bairooni, he wrote an essay on how to define the chord in a circle. Most of these Arabic books were translated by the Europeans into Latin since the 12th century A.D. I would like to mention one person in particular Adelard of Bath, who translated 'The Tables of Trigonometry Calculus' by Al Khawarizmi in the year AD 1162. and also translated other trigonometry books.

The knowledge of Arabic in the science of mechanics is also great and wide, and, as a proof of that, we can see the remains of their machines and their description of these machines in the books they left. The Arabs were also engaged in the translation of the Greek writings, and this engagement continued until the 13th century A.D. when Al Toosi translated the book of 'The Moving Ball' by Utolycus. But the Arabs contributed more to this knowledge, and some European scientists believe the Arabs invented the clock's pendulum and used the pendulum in measuring time. This means the Arabs knew the heavy clocks, which are different from water clocks as is clear in the description of the clock in the Amawi Mosque in Damascus which can be found in some referral sources.

The conclusion is that Arabs were very advanced in mathematics and Europe benefited from them greatly in this field. Any close reader of any of the Arabs' books in mathematics will be astonished at the advancement of Arabs and the wide knowledge they had attained and the accuracy of their research. Al Khawarizmi, for example, was involved in explaining the equations of two and three dimensions to a great extent and his reasoning was very scientific and his explanation was copious. He also looked into the roots and the way the area of different shapes, such as triangles, squares, circles and rhombi is calculated. He then moved on to complicated matters and defined the way to solve them in a skilful and accurate way that is truly fascinating.

Chapter Two

The role of Arab Muslim scientists
in developing the final shape of our
Arabic Numerals and their usages which
have been wide in all corners of the globe

The use of Arabic Numerals has become one of the topics where there is a need to shed some light on the role of Arab Muslim scientists in developing these numerals and the influence they left on human civilization.

There are questions raised sometimes among intellectuals about the shape of Arabic Numerals. Are they the oriental current numbers (shown below)?

١ ٢ ٣ ٤ ٥ ٦ ٧ ٨ ٩ ٠

Or are they the Arabic Numerals which are used in most countries of the world as well as some of the Arab countries of North Africa (shown below)?

1 2 3 4 5 6 7 8 9 0

The reason for this question leads us to a study that makes clear the role of the Arabs in using the numerals and to emphasize the civilized role of the Arab Muslims in the development of our Arabic Numerals.

For this purpose, it is important to divide this study into the following sections.

• The use of numbers across eras
• The Arab's use of numbers
• The study's recommendations

The use of numbers across eras

The Arab Islamic civilization, like any other civilization, was influenced by previous civilizations and it has influenced subsequent civilizations. The Arabs acknowledge the merit of previous civilizations and their influence on them. Therefore, the Arabic Islamic civilization was not born out of mere chance or without advanced preparation. Mathematics and the transfer of arithmetic, and consequently the numbers in particular, have left a clear impact on Arabic Islamic civilization. I shall go through the shapes and forms of these numbers and how they changed over the years, right from the ancient times of the Egyptians, Babylonians, Greeks, Chinese, Romans and Indians.

1- The Ancient Egyptian Numerical System

For over 5000 years, the ancient Egyptians used symbols for numbers: one, ten, one hundred, one thousand, one hundred thousand, and one million. They didn't have a symbol for zero. Their numerical system didn't recognize the positional value (units, tens,…etc). Instead, the symbol was repeated several times, perhaps in a way that we might find very simple now after the invention of the decimal system, the symbol of zero and the idea of positional or local value. Hieroglyphic language was the language of ancient Egyptians and the symbols of numbers in that language were written as in the shapes below:

Numerical example

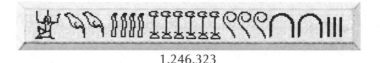

1.246.323

All Greek writers agreed unanimously that Egypt was the first country to invent all mathematical sciences. *Plato* mentioned that the Egyptian God, *Tutankhamun,* was the inventor of many arts among which were arithmetic, trigonometry and astronomy. *Aristotle* said that Egypt was the birth place of mathematics, because the priests' class had ample spare time which allowed them to study the science of mathematics. *Herodotus* also concluded that trigonometry started in Egypt and then it was transferred to Greece. The first referral authoritative source on mathematics was the 'Egyptian Mathematical papyrus' which is also called 'The Rhind Mathematical Papyrus' in the west and known in Arabic as *Qurtas Ahis*. This was discovered by *Alexander Henry Rhind* in 1858 and translated by Eisenlohr in 1877 and edited by *Eric Peet* in 1923. This book was from the era of the second dynasty (1801 / 1849 B.C.). Birch believes that the information in the book goes back to 3400 B.C. The author called it 'Instructions for Knowing All Things Available'.

The book has five chapters and 87 mathematical problems:

- First chapter: Counting and number writing
- Second Chapter: The Four Rules
- Third Chapter: Decimals
- Fourth Chapter: Square, root square, problem solving of the first degree, and the series.
- Fifth Chapter: Engineering

2- Numbers in Mesopotamia (The Land between Two Rivers)

Old stamps were found in miscellaneous places which indicate the existence of trade relations between the Sumerians, the most ancient among the people of Mesopotamia, and both Egypt and India. Many sheets of mud were also found with Sumerian writings on them. This reveals that there was an active trade movement where there were contracts and witnesses to those contracts, as well as documents that reveal the methods of taking loans and interests on those loans, which were between 25% and 33% per year. It seems that the Sumerians have taken the sciences of arithmetic from the ancient Egyptians, but the opposite is probably true as well. However the Sumerians were able to invent the numbers in 3700 B.C. in Tel Harmal in Iraq. What we have found is a text that was left by a person with the name of Ashoor Panipal in which he said he learnt how to find common denominators and how to perform arithmetical operations. There is another text under the title 'Scientific Matters' which talks about the methods of teaching mathematics in schools and times tables.

The Babylonians came after the Sumerians and inherited from them the knowledge of numbers around 2400 B.C. and then the Assyrians came afterwards. The peoples of Mesopotamia attached a high importance to numbers. They were able to set many admirable arithmetic rules. They also wrote numbers of pottery disks using sharp machines in a horizontal line from right to left. They also used signs which refer to subtraction, for example, the number 19 was written 20 minus one. The Romans did the same thing afterwards.

The symbols they used were known as 'cuneiform writing' as the symbol for number one was like a 'standing nail' that is repeated between numbers 'one' and 'nine'. The symbol for number 'ten' was like this shape ' ⟨ ', while number 'eleven' was written as number 'ten', with the shape of number 'one' (the nail shape) written to the right of it. The number 'one hundred' was written like the shape of two lines, as in the following shape; ' ⊤ ' where one of the lines on the left is perpendicular and the other one on the right is horizontal. The number 'one thousand' was pictured as if it was 'ten hundreds' as in the following shape: ' ' , and if you write the number 'ten' next to it, the total value will become 'ten thousands' and so on and so forth. The words for numbers from 'one' to 'five' are the same as the words for the hand figures. They are as follows:

1 = Ash
2 = Men
3 = Ish
4 = Lemu
5 = Ay Away

They added the word 'Ay' to the first digits to mean an increase of 'five', so they became as follows:

6 = Yash or (Ay Ash)
7 = Ay Men
8 = Ayshu (Ay Shu
9 = Almu or (Ay Mu)

Number 'ten' was referred to as (Aw), while 'twenty', the double of ten, was 'Nesh'. From 'ten' and its structures, came the following numbers:

30 = Aw Shu (which means three tens)
40 = Nesh Men (two times twenty)
50 = Ninu (nini Aw) or (2 X 20 + 10)

This way the Sumerians, and those who came after them, developed the decimal system and invented the Sixtieth System and they used it as a numerical unit when they saw that the circle's perimeter was divisible to six equal chords, each one is equal to half of circle's diameter. They discovered this after they noticed that the shape of a bee cell was hexagonal.
They also noticed that the circle was divided into six triangles, all have equal sides, where angles were measured in degrees and every angle was 60 degrees. This division of the circle into angles coincided with the division of the year in an astonishing coincident: 360 days = 6 X 60.

Source: www.alargam.com

3 - Numbers in China

The Chinese were the first to put the local value for a digit, or what is called digital place, and they paved the way for the Indians to invent the Indian Numerals which we use now. Let us now explain the shapes of the Chinese numerals:

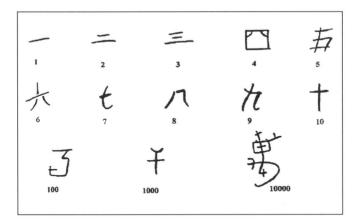

The Chinese system of numeric symbols is made of the symbols used in the Chinese language for writing numbers. These symbols represent numbers from zero to nine, and there are other symbols which represent bigger numbers such as tens, hundreds and thousands and so on. There are two types of symbols used in the Chinese numerical system: The first is for daily use in writing, and the second is used in commercial or financial transactions which are known in China as 'Dasia' (see the table below). The Chinese numerical system today is based on the same method that is used in forming words which is indicative of numbers in the English language.

	0	1	2	3	4	5	6	7	8	9	10	100	1000
Traditional (used in Hong Kong and Taiwan)	零	一	二	三	四	五	六	七	八	九	十	百	千
Simplified (used in Mainland China)	零	一	二	三	四	五	六	七	八	九	十	百	千
Official Traditional-Dasia (used in Hong Kong and Taiwan)	零	壹	貳	參	肆	伍	陸	柒	捌	玖	拾	佰	仟
Official Simplified-Dasia (used in Mainland China)	零	壹	贰	参	肆	伍	陆	柒	捌	玖	拾	佰	仟

Chapter 2

Arabic Numerals were first introduced to China during the reign of the Ming Dynasty (1368 – 1644). During the reign of the King Dynasty (1644 - 1912), the system of Chinese numeric symbols was replaced with Arabic Numerals in mathematical writings. Children in China today learn Chinese numeric symbols through Chinese language lessons. Arabic numerals are used in all mathematical studies.

It is worth mentioning that the system of traditional Chinese numerical symbols is the same system that is used in Japan and Korea. It is used in the vertical texts in these countries, while Arabic numerals are used in horizontal texts and in mathematical writings which are more common. Sometimes, the system of traditional Chinese numerical symbols is used alongside the Arabic Numerals on the same page. The Chinese people use Chinese numerals in the same way the Western cultures use the Roman numerals i.e. for official use and also for historical and artistic reasons. From an artistic point of view, the Chinese numerals do have a beautiful calligraphy.

4 - The Greek Numerical System

There is no doubt that the Greeks played an outstanding role in the progress of the material civilization, but we must know that they benefited a lot from the civilizations which preceded them, such as the Sumerian, Assyrian, Babylonian, Ancient Egyptian, and Indian. They also benefited from Phoenicians who used numerical letters in the first millennium before Christ. The Greeks learned writing from Phoenicians, as they didn't know it before that time, and they used the Phoenician letters in their writing for a long time. They also used the letters to express numerical values, i.e. using letters instead of numbers, until their language changed by the passage of time which had also led to a change in numbers.

The Greeks and the Romans used the decimal system of counting, and they also wrote their numbers from left to right. There is some similarity between the Greek and Roman numerals. Examine the table below:

The shapes of Greek numbers (to be entered into the first row of the table)

Their numerical value (to be entered into the second row)

ᴹ̄	M	X̄	X	ᴴ̄	H	Δ̄	Δ	Γ	I	أشكال الأرقام عند الإغريق
50000	10000	5000	1000	500	100	50	10	5	1	القيمة العددية لها

We can see that in the 'five' category, with the exception of 'five' itself, which are '50, 500, 5000, 50000', the 'five' was combined with 'ten', the 'five' with the 'hundred', the 'five' with the 'thousand', and the 'five' with the 'ten thousand' respectively.

The Ionists, who were members of the 'Ion' Greek tribe, used their letters to express numbers, and they distinguished between a letter and a number by putting a sign above the number.

The Ptolemaic dynasty, or the Egyptian Greeks, knew 'zero' and they pictured it like this shape 'O'. They must have acquired it through the Sixtieth System from the Babylonians (Dr Albert Dietrich in his article 'The Role of the Arabs in the Development of Natural Sciences' – 'The Greeks learned a lot of information in the sciences of mathematics, astronomy and medicine, from the Egyptians and Babylonians'). Or, they had learned the zero from the Indians, or perhaps they had invented it.

The Greeks (and also the Arabs and the Hebraic) used their alphabetical letters to represent numbers. To explain the Greek system clearly, we will use the letters alpha α , beta β , iota ι , and kappa κ , which represent the numbers 'one', 'two' … 'ten', 'twenty' respectively. While $\iota\beta$ refers to 'ten and two' or 12, it is not possible to exchange them as in the case of the current symbols. We can now change the number 12 to mean 21 to refer to the number 'twenty one' by using the two digits (1 and 2) interchangeably. In the Greek system, the number 'twenty one' is represented by the symbol $\kappa\alpha$. Because the Greeks didn't work out the idea of positional or local value, they had to use all twenty four alphabetical letters, in addition to three other symbols, to write the basic numbers. They are Γ (gamma) to represent number 'five', H (ita) to represent '100', X ,(khi) to represent 1000. These numbers are repeated when writing any other number using the method of 'assembly' as the ancient Egyptians did. As time went by, the Greeks found a method that allowed them to abbreviate symbols. This is called 'multiplication method' for writing numbers. For example, 'H' means 'five hundreds'. It is noticeable that this method is not used unless for the expression of a number that is the product of multiplication by 'five'. Examine the table below:

Chapter 2

Name of Letter	Small Letter	Capital Letter
Alpa	α	A
Beta	β	B
gamma	γ	Γ
delta	δ	Δ
epsilon	ε	E
zeta	ζ	Z
eta	η	H
theta	θ	Θ
iota	ι	I
kappa	κ	K
lambda	λ	Λ
Mu	μ	M
Nu	ν	N
xi	ξ	Ξ
Omicron	o	O
rho	ρ	P
pi	π	Π
sigma	σ	Σ
tau	τ	T
upsilon	υ	Υ
phi	φ	Φ
chi	χ	X
psi	ψ	Ψ
omega	ω	Ω

One of God's blessings to the Greeks is that they made commercial contacts with ancient nations, which enabled them to learn the philosophy of these nations as well as their arts and myths. When trade between them and the Egyptians was active during the seventh century B.C. they were exposed to the knowledge of Egyptian priests. This way Egyptian thoughts were transferred overseas into the land of the Greeks.

Their method of writing numbers was similar to that of ancient Egyptians. They then used alphabetical letters to express numbers – that's why their arithmetic was so complicated. Below is the shape of numbers that the Greeks used:

I	△	H	X	M
1	10	100	1000	10000
⌐	⌈△	⌈H	⌈X	
5	50	500	5000	

(The shape of numbers the Greeks used is similar
to the method used by ancient Egyptians)

5 - Roman Numerical System

The Roman numerical system was influenced by the idea of 'local value' – as we will see – and it is thought that the basis for the Roman numerical system was counting by fingers. What led to this belief is that the word for finger in Latin is *jigitus*, a derivative of which is now used to describe any of their numerical symbols, which is the word *digit*. The Romans wrote the numbers from *one* to *four* as follows:

I   II   III   IIII

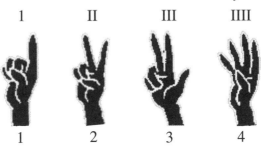

1   2   3   4

As for the symbol for number *five*, it was written like this *V* and this may represent the gap between the thumb and the rest of the fingers as in the shape below:

V

5

Chapter 2

The local value was formed by them while it was closely connected to this symbol, and in order to avoid writing the number '1' four times they wrote '1' to the left of 'V' and the same idea was applied to other symbols. It had become clear ever since that when a symbol is written to the left of another symbol whose value is higher, then the number refers to the difference between the two symbols. When it is written to the right of it, then the new number refers to the sum of the two symbols. On this basis, the numbers 6, 7, and 8 were expressed, as in the illustrative shape below:

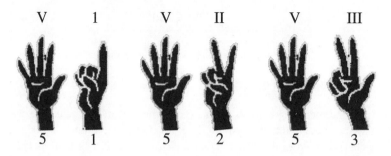

To express the digit '9', the symbol '1' is written on the left of the symbol for the digit 'ten' which is 'X', the shape of which may have been taken from the position of the two hands crossed. Number '9' is written as such: '1X', while number '10' is written as 'X', then the number '11' which is referred to by the symbol 'X1' where the symbol expressing number '1' is written to the right of the symbol of number '10' so that both will refer to the sum of both numbers, and so on. On this basis, the first Roman numerals were as follows:

The first Roman Numerals	I	II	III	IV	V	VI	VII	VIII	IX
Their counterparts in modern numbers	1	2	3	4	5	6	7	8	9
The First Roman Numbers					X	XI	XII	XIII	XIV
Their counterparts in modern numbers					10	11	12	13	14

This method is followed until you reach the number 'twenty' which is expressed as 'XX' then 'thirty' which is expressed as 'XXX'.

In order to avoid the repetition of a digit four times to express '40' as (XXXX), the symbol 'L' was adopted to express number fifty. It is thought that it is the bottom half of the letter C which refers to the number 'hundred' and it is the first letter of the word '*Centum*' (or hundred) in Latin. Therefore, the number 40 is written like this 'XL' while the symbol 'LX' refers to number sixty. Also, the symbol 'XC' refers to number '90' while 'CX' refers to 'hundred and ten' or (110). Then, the letter M was used to refer to the number 'one thousand' (1000), and this is probably because it is the first letter of the Latin word '*Mille*' which means one thousand (1000). Before that, the number 'one thousand' was expressed by the Greek letter phi Φ, then it was written in a simple form like this 'I', and this was altered again to 'M' to express the number 1000. As for the number 500, it was expressed by the symbol | ⟩ and this, as you can see, is the right part of the Greek letter pi (I) in its simple form. Then the symbol | ⟩ which refers to 500 altered to the letter D. The following table shows briefly the basic symbols of the Roman numerical system.

M	D	C	L	X	V	I
1000	500	100	50	10	5	1

On this basis, the Latin number 'MXDVIII' refers to the number 1408 in modern numerical system, and the number 'MMCCCXXLV' refers to 2335, and the year '1999' is expressed like this: MCMXCIX, and so on.

Sources: www.alargam.com

6 - Indian Numbers

There is a group of old Indian numbers called 'Popular Karoshti' and this began in the third century B.C. and then it took certain clear shapes in two centuries, but it is not based on a hierarchical idea. Smith and Karpinski (David Eugene Smith and Louis Charles Karpinski) found a similarity between these shapes and the Nabati letters, but they ruled out that the Karoshti shapes were the origin of the Indian numbers which in the end reached the Arabs and the Europeans. Below are some of these shapes:

Chapter 2

As for the other group that was referred to by Smith and Karpinski, it is the Brahmi group of numbers and they regarded it as the origin from which the Devanagari alphabet was derived.

(Dr Sa'eedan said in his study: (The Arithmetic Science Among The Ancient Arabs) on page 180, quoting Smith and Karpinski:

'The pictures of numbers seem to have come from the pictures of Devanagari alphabet, which form the origin of Sanskrit alphabet, which is, in its part, used to write the Brahmi language'. Dr Bukhari also mentioned in his book (Arabic Numerals), on page 34 that the use of the Brahmi alphabet spread widely in all parts of India during the third century B.C. (it's A.D. in Dr Bukhari's book) but it's highly likely that what I said was more accurate. He reckons that the arithmetic and numbering system among the Arabs, page 80, volume 4, began when Asoka unified all parts of India.

They, the Brahmi group of numbers, are the origin of the present Sanskrit numbers. But Smith and Karpinski could not confirm that they are the origin of the Arabic numbers.

Dr Sa'eedan continued talking about the views of Western researches during those stages saying 'As for Drainger, his main concern was to study the history of alphabets and their development. As far as the Karoshti Alphabet was concerned, he confirmed that it was the alphabet of the common people who used it in their daily life; therefore, we should not wait to see it on manuscripts and religious writings. He also confirmed that it used to start from right to left until at a later time, the direction of writing was reversed. The Karoshti alphabet was used in eastern Afghanistan and southern Punjab. Drainger thinks it was derived from the Aramaic letters... As for the Brahmi Alphabet, he, Drainger, thinks it's likely that it was derived from the Aramaic Alphabet '.

Dr Bukhari showed some examples of ancient Brahmi numbers as shown below:

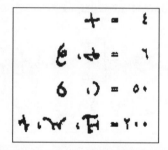

He later showed the shapes of the developed Brahmi numbers, which were used
since the twelfth century A.D. They are as follows:

?	५	٦	ﻉ	ﻉ	✶	=	=	—
٩	٨	٧	٦	٥	٤	٣	٢	١ : الآحاد
⊕	⊙	Ⴟ	ﻉ	J	X	ᴦ	♂	α
٩٠	٨٠	٧٠	٦٠	٥٠	٤٠	٣٠	٢٠	١٠ : العشرات
		𝒲	⅀	ꝯ	ﱟ	ﭞ	ﱟ	
		٧٠٠٠	٤٠٠٠	١٠٠٠	٥٠٠	٢٠٠	١٠٠ : المئات والألوف

He then tried to show the sets of shapes of the Nijari numbers (from the
region of Nijari) according to the stages of their development, adding that the
older types of these numbers are similar to Brahmi Numbers. He showed
them as follows:

Dr Abdussattar Muhammed Faidh showed two sets of shapes for Indian
numbers, and they looked like the shapes below:

—	=	≡	⧺	ﻉ	٦	?	٦	٢	٥ : الشكل الأول
٩	٢	٢	৪	४	٤	٦	٢	٢	٥ : الشكل الثاني

Chapter 2

As for the shapes of Indian numbers as mentioned by the oldest Arabic books – that reached us – in the Indian Arithmetic the first Arabic book in arithmetic was that of Muhammed Bin Musa Al Khawarizmi, and it is now missing, although many of the Latin manuscripts quoted it and took some excerpts from it. But the numbers and arithmetic operations within those Latin letters, which were presumed to have been done by Al Khawarizmi, are very different to what was known among the Arabs – in the East and West – whether they were numbers or the way of calculation. Source: 'The Story of Numbers and Numbering', pages 68-69, and the study entitled 'The Science of Arithmetic Among the Arabs', pages 181-182.

Let me now explain some more facts through what the following books have said about numbers:

In the book 'Al Fusool Fi Al Hissab Al Hindi' or 'Chapters in Indian Arithmetic' by Abi Al Hassan Ahmed Bin Ibrahim Al Iqleedsi which was the first to reach us from those books, and the author wrote it in Damascus in the year 341 Hijra, we find:

The First section: In the knowledge of the Nine Letters and the Ranks: The first thing that must be learnt of that by anyone who began learning this science is learning the nine letters, and these are as follows:

Source: www.alargam.com

The Use of Numbers Among the Arab Muslims

The interest Muslims showed in mathematics and other different sciences was mostly due to the teachings of Islam. These teachings encouraged, and still do, learning in all its forms and levels. The Quraan says 'Seeking Knowledge is a duty on every Muslim man and woman'. While the Prophet Muhammed said "Seek Knowledge even if it was in China", signifying the importance of knowledge and extent to which people should go in acquiring it. Also, the Holy Quraan has urged people to look at the skies and what they contain, and to the earth and what is on it. Personal status issues also required Muslims to look into many things such as inheritance, commercial transactions, contracts and their expiry dates, knowledge of calendars, arithmetic and calculus. Worship also required knowing the times of prayers, identifying the direction of Mecca (the Ka'aba) and knowing the time

when the crescent appears signalling the start of Ramadan and the time of Hajj
(pilgrimage to Mecca) etc. which required Muslims to follow the movements of
the sun and the moon. All this made the Muslims search for knowledge and
science, especially astronomy which requires knowledge of all different forms of
mathematics, from calculus to trigonometry to algebra, and all that is related to
the sciences of nature and metaphysics.

How did Arabs make contacts with other civilizations?

The Arabs made contacts with the Greeks via the ancient Syrians in Asia Minor.
Through them they made contacts with the Christian Greeks, and also through
travels and tours. The caliphs also brought Greek scientists who translated Greek
knowledge and science into the Arabic language. The Arabs also made contacts
with the Persians and Indians, and they were closely associated with them. This
way the Arab's knowledge, culture and civilization became deep and multi
dimensional. During the reign of Caliph Othman Bin Affan, the Arabs were in
contact with the Indians, and also during the conquest of Sind by Hajjaj Bin
Yousif Ath-Thiqafi in AD 710. and the conquest of Kabul and Kashmir by Caliph
Abu Ja'afar Al Mansour in the year AD 760.

Researchers believe that the Arab's influence on humanity is huge for the
following reasons:

1- The Arabs were faithful and honest keepers of Greek scientific treasures.
They kept them intact and prosperous (by advancing them), and they saved
them from the Romans.

2- They were responsible for spreading the Indian scientific treasures which
prospered in the east while the Greek sciences prospered in the west.

3- They made the connection between the Greek and Indian sciences and built
on both of them to create new coherent sets of ideas, and they handed all this
knowledge, pure and intact, to westerners when they woke up from their
dormancy and 'took off the jacket' of apathy. They, westerners, marched into
Andalusia to study at the universities of Seville, Cordoba and Granada which
were established by the Arabs. They also went to other places in search of
knowledge and science, and learned the Arabic language in order to study
developed sciences and other types of knowledge at Arabic universities. Those
western students, for their part, transferred what they had learned from the
Arabs into Latin.

4- The Arabs added to the knowledge and sciences that they received from others, more radiant scientific conquests and new valuable discoveries; although these were wrongly attributed to others and some thought they were discovered afterwards.

What is the story of Arabic Numerals?

There is no doubt that the Arab Muslims, as is the case with all other peoples within civilizations, influenced others and were influenced by others. But it's a mistake for some people to believe that the Arabic Numerals are Indian, or the zero (0), or cipher, is not Arabic, or that Arabic Numerals should be written like this:

١ ٢ ٣ ٥ ٤ ٦ ٧ ٨ ٩ ٠

This is because scientific matters have been confused, to a great extent, and they have become so ambiguous to so many people. The story began when the Arabs got to know the different systems of numbering that were used by other peoples whom they conquered and with whom they established friendships. They preferred the Indian system, even though the Indians had many shapes for numbers, but the Arabs selected what they thought proper and they decided to have two different ways of writing the numbers:

1- The Eastern or Oriental Way, and this was used by the Baghdad Arabs, and it developed briefly until the numbers shown below became common in Egypt, Iraq, Syria, Lebanon, Palestine, and all Arab countries:

١ ٢ ٣ ٥ ٤ ٦ ٧ ٨ ٩ ٠

2- The Western Way, and this was used by the Arabs of the Andalus (Andalusia in Spain) and it developed somewhat until the use of the numbers shown below became common in the Arab West: 1 2 3 4 5 6 7 8 9 0

The Western World took the Arab West's method of writing the numbers through Andalusia but they reversed the chronology so that it conformed to the way they wrote their words.

The Western Arabs (North Africans) still write the numbers in the same way their ancestors did. It should not be thought by anyone that they are using the Francophone numerals; on the contrary, the westerners (Europeans) are the ones who are writing their numbers according to the Arab Westerners' (North Africans) way. The West still calls these numerals (Arabic Numerals).

What is the story of the (zero) for the Muslims?

Many researchers deny that the number 'zero' was an Indian concept; while others insist it was an Arabic one. The truth is that the value of the 'zero' and other numbers is not actually in the shapes of the numbers but in the acquired value. We can now, through the multiple use of the 'zero', express the highest value numbers as well as the lowest value numbers. It suffices that we increase the number of 'zeros' on the right of the fraction to make it smaller and smaller.

Some researchers believe that the shape of the 'zero' that was used by the Indians was like a circle with a dot in the middle, such as this one: ⊙ i.e. it was an empty space. And this use came at later times. But the Eastern Arabs took up the 'dot' and left the circle out, while the Western Arabs, took up the circle and left the dot out.

Some other researchers believe that Muslim mathematicians knew the Greek shape of the 'zero' which is a circle with a line on the top. Some calligraphers linked the line at the top to the circle in their writings.

On this basis, the shape of the zero in the Greek alphabet is basically the same as the Indian one, especially if we know that the Indian tradition of writing numbers is based on drawing a line above the digit. In spite of all this, and as I said at the beginning regarding the 'zero', the Arabs were the ones who defined both the value and use of the 'zero'. As for its shape, it is a mere transfer from one civilization to another, and before that, it was one choice among many other possible choices, and it was a development of a concept to reach its final shape, until the Arabs had their own numbers, whether they were written according to western or eastern way.

A Study Reveals the Secret of Arabic Numerals

We have received from Mr Abdul Hay Ad-Dakali from Morocco an address of a site for numbers where there is a study of numbers that reveals the secrets of the Arabic Numerals which we would like to show to you below:

In this table, the alphabet letter takes the value of the number opposite to it.

Table of Sentence Calculations

The Arabs used the arithmetic calculations of sentences from the Jahili era (the period that preceded Islam) to the early years of the Abbasid era (Source: Arab International Encyclopaedia). Sentence calculations were used mostly for writing down events.

Chapter 2

opposing number	Alphabetic letter	opposing number	Alphabetic letter
20	ك	1	أ
30	ل	2	ب
40	م	3	ج
50	ن	4	د
60	س	5	ه
70	ع	6	و
80	ف	7	ز
90	ص	8	ح
100	ق	9	ط
200	ر	10	ي
400	ت	300	ش
600	خ	500	ث
800	ض	700	ذ
1000	غ	900	ظ

If we add up the values of letters with two arithmetic aims, as below, we will get 176: 2 + 1 + 60 + 8 + 10 + 80 + 4 + 5 + 6

The year 176, according to the Hijri calendar, was in the period when Idrees the First ruled Morocco from 172 until 177 Hijri, and in the period where Haroon Ar Rasheed ruled the Arab East, from 170 until 193 Hijri.

In the year 176 Hijri, the Kufi calligraphy was in vogue. This name is used for all the calligraphies which tend to have squares and trigonometric shapes. The shape below is a Kufi calligraphy

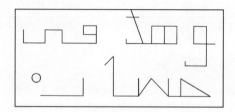

When we decipher this sentence into letters we will get the following:

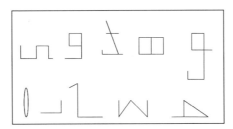

This means the following:

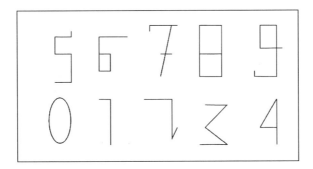

And if the letter (waw= و) and the voul (sukoon= ˚) were left as they are, and if we move the letters (ha'a= هـ), (fa'a= ف), (ya'a= ي), (ha'a= ح), (seen= س), (alif= ا) and (ba'a= ب), and if we turned over the letter (dal = د), we will get the Arabic Numerals:

1 2 3 4 5 6 7 8 9 0

All the numbers have remained as they are today except the number 2. If we turned it upside down, we will get the letter (ha'a = ح) which is the sixth letter of the Arabic alphabet.

Chapter Three

Globalization and Numbers

1- In Economics: Local and international economy depends on numbers and 50% of the business language in all nations depends on numbers, while the rest is just explanation of these numbers and they are explanations and expressions with unified known meanings.

2 - In Mathematics: Mathematics depends on numbers by no less than 70% while letters used in mathematics represent only 15%, while the remainder is for signs such as plus, minus, *equal, percentage* etc… (+ , - ,= , %).

3- Electronics and the sciences of communication also depend totally on numbers.

4- Chemistry and other sciences such as civil registers and others depend on numbers.

5- Most countries of the world, with the exception of countries of the Arab Orient, use the Arabic Numerals which we called in this book Our Arabic Numerals since they have become the common language of numbers among the nations using them.

6- The Number 'zero' which in fact constitutes the dynamic force for all numbers, but is actually a cause for making many mistakes in the oriental numbers as it is often confused with dots and other similar writing symbols. Also, when it disappears or doesn't come out clearly in writings or printings, it causes problems and it is actually a flaw in our oriental numbers.

7- Most civilized writings are bound to depend on using numbers at different rates. The only places where numbers are not widely used are literal and historical books and articles and some novels.

8- If our nation wishes to enter globalization and introduce its heritage and civilization to the world, it must change its current oriental numerals to our Arabic Numerals. This way, the language of communication between nations will be easier by 50%. This will also facilitate the tasks of researchers and readers, and consequently the benefit in the fields of creativity in art and production will be increased by 50%.

Finally, every negative aspect in our oriental numbers, from their shapes to the isolation they impose on their users, from the march of civilization of numbers, will be positive when change into our Arabic Numerals is effected.

Chapter Four

The Leaders who made the change and developed civilizations across history

Nations do not rise from their mistakes or decline except through great scientific, technological and cultural revolutions that their sons and daughters achieve and spread or their leaders carry out and implement. Let us review what has been happening across the ages and in our current time:

1- If we look closely at the subject of number development in this book, we will find that across history there is someone who has thought and excelled and leaders who have implemented the innovations of individuals. They are the ones who started the revolutionary changes in their civilizations.

2- The study in this book reveals some aspects of number development and its contribution to modern technological sciences. If it was not for the development of numbers, in both shape and meaning, and their contribution to what humanity has reached, we would not have attained this great honour today where numbers are referred to as Arabic Numerals. The numbers are the best ammunition and best Islamic treasures that the Muslims bequeathed after they were defeated in Europe. Is it not time to reclaim these treasures and benefit from them? Especially after Arabic numbers have become the magic keys to modern technological sciences in the form that is prevalent today worldwide?

3- As the Holy Quraanic verse (We taught man what he didn't know; Soorat Al Alaq, verse number 5) says, knowledge comes from God, but the will to work comes from us human beings. All holy verses have urged people to do good deeds as the holy Quraanic verse says (Good deeds lasts on earth…etc. Surat Ar Ra'ad, verse number 177).

4- I saw a film on the life of Hitler that was shown in Germany in the nineteen fifties after World War 2. It was shown in every city at the time in more than three cinemas. The turnout was large, especially among the youth. The film was about Hitler's life since his appearance on the political stage, and most of the footage was from real events that were shot during his lifetime, while others were shot for the sake of chronological coherence of the story in the film. Most parts of the film were focused on the technical and development revolutions that took place in his time. It also showed the war that he fought which affected everything except the brains which remained in force to enlighten Germany and set it again at the forefront of other nations. The conclusion of the film was that if Hitler hadn't entered politics, he would have probably been the greatest and most multi- talented engineer humanity had ever witnessed.

There is no surprise there as Bismarck preceded him in unifying Germany, while Goethe also preceded him by unifying the language and setting the grammar for it.

Chapter 4

Today, as I am still perplexed (which I have been for many months before I began writing this book) whose idea has been on my mind for many years, there was a news story circulating in the news bulletins. It is about a decree issued in Germany, for more than a year, that sets new grammar for writing and dictation for more than two hundred common German words. This meant that the new grammar rules would alter the letters used in the composition of these words to make them easier to learn or remember. German linguists, in this day and age, are alert even to the rules of their language which is supposed to be the symbol of their glories and pride. The political leaders of the country have expressed their highest appreciation for the linguists on their move and stated their willingness to adopt these grammar changes. The news story was about those people who were opposing the introduction of the new grammar changes. The opposition was mostly from publishing houses which will be affected because their publications of school text books and other stationery wouldn't be sold if the changes were adopted. They had a different view regarding education. I would like to show the readers what one newspaper carried regarding this issue:

Spelling and reading grammar in the German language:

The language that has no speakers or writers will head towards extinction

No sooner had the application of the new rules began than they were confronted with sharp criticism in all parts of Germany, Austria and Switzerland. These rules were intended to make the use of the language easier. Yet, German speakers described them as 'confusing' and 'silly'.

The German News Agency said that this change affects 212 spelling rules and 52 other rules on the place of the 'comma' and this led to the reduction of the spelling rules to 112 and comma rules to just 9 in a language that is heavily restricted by hundreds of other rules which are complicated and strange in their structures.

The defenders of the new system say it will make education easier and it will help in the documentation process in offices and government administrations.

The new system will allow, during a transitional period that will last till 2005, the use of the new and old rules together. Those opposing the change, who are mostly older people, can continue to use what is politely called 'the traditional writing'.

Gabriel Beihler, who presided over a meeting in Vienna for the ministers of cultures of German speaking countries in 1996 during which they agreed on the new rules, called upon the media and writers to cooperate in implementing and developing the new grammar rules and guidelines.

On the other hand, the opponents of the change didn't spare any effort to condemn the new grammar rules which they said were not logical nor smooth. In addition, they said the new rules will deprive the German language of its rich legacy. Gabriel Rota, the spokesman for the opponents of the new measure, called on the authorities to ban the new grammar rules and ignore them completely in the coming months on the basis that 'the language that doesn't find users to write in it will head towards extinction.

Millions of German Deutsche Marks were spent on new text books based on the amended grammar and the Constitutional Court in Germany rejected an appeal to ban the new rules from taking effect on the grounds that they violate basic freedoms.

The appeal that the court looked at, which was lodged by a couple from the northern city of Lübeck, said the changes represent an infringement of their legal rights in the direction of teaching their children who were 9 years old.

While in the state of Schlezwich Hew Lischtein in the far north of Germany, a referendum was held on 27th September, the same day of the general election in the whole country, on whether to implement the new rules in the state or not.

Hostile feelings to the linguistic reforms were at their highest among students, experts and parents who were demanding of their local government to keep Schlezwich Hew Lischtein the odd state separate from all German states. They wanted it to continue to work according to the 'authentic' grammar system of the German language.

The prime motive for the reforms was that the German language, in its composition when the reforms were introduced, was based on hundreds of grammar rules which do not follow specific logic or general rules and this made memorizing these rules or learning them very difficult. This means that learning the language by heart was a must for German children as well as for those who wanted to learn the language among non- Germans.

The collapse of the Berlin wall represented a huge shock to the world. No sooner had the unity between the two German states been announced, than the government of Federal Germany employed all its economic powers to cement the unity in spite of the high cost to the western part of the country and the economic suffering that was inflicted on its people, and in spite of the differences that accumulated in abilities and ethics between the people of the two former German states.

Germany didn't stop at internal revolutionary reforms in the fields of science and economics, but it employed its economic power and its former currency

Chapter 4

(the Deutsche Mark) in the service of the unification of European countries. The most important achievement of the European unity is the 'Euro', and no two persons would disagree that the German Mark and German economy were the catalysts behind the achievement of the 'Euro'. In addition to the economic costs, what sorts of scientific and technical knowledge, technologies, organization, promotion, and naturalization that the Euro required to replace 25 different currencies, in the literal sense of the word differentiate, in form, content, application and value? They must have been very huge. How did this change to the European currencies facilitate life for the people of the 'Euro' region and help them improve their life, present and future? Isn't the Euro an economic and civilizational unifying revolution that transformed the citizens of these countries from one world to another? Yes, that was the achievement of leaders who were chosen by their people and they were indeed the right choice.

5- Although I do not approve of the change that Mutafa Kamal Ataturk made (when he took over the rule in Turkey after the collapse of the Ottoman empire), in replacing the Arabic alphabet with the Latin alphabet in the Turkish language, this has in fact stripped the Turkish people of their identity and resulted in Turkish generations losing contact with their civilization and sciences. In that change, they lost what distinguished them from other nations. I say, despite my disapproval of this step, that I must acknowledge it was a bold step to replace the Arabic alphabet with the Latin alphabet as a means to revive Turkish fortunes and stamp out decay and backwardness in Turkey which were due to the long traditional rule of the successive Ottoman caliphs.

6- In spite of what is known about the British people and their conservative policies it is their lack of enthusiasm for change as well as their coolness that distinguishes them from other people. An example of this is their official holidays which are always moved to a Monday whenever they fall during the week. They are called Bank Holidays. Ordinary people do not really know the occasions of these holidays except for Christmas and New Year as these two holidays are celebrated on the exact date that they fall. I say, in spite of this conservatism, many rules and basis for measurements of length and weight have been changed. The currency has also been changed in 1971 from shillings and guineas (the shilling was based on 12 whereas the decimal currency is based on 10). Also, measurements of length have been changed from 'foot', 'yard' and 'mile', to metric measurements. Weight measurements have also been changed form 'ounce' and 'pound' to decimal measurements which are gram and kilogram. Although these changes were not sudden the change went quietly. The difference between the German way of changing things and the British way is that the former is speedy in implementation and revolutionary in nature while the latter is quiet and patient. But the important point for both is that they reached the set targets.

Chapter Five

The Development of Our Arabic Numbers in the Era of Computers

At a time when the Arab West, such as the countries of Morocco, Tunisia, and Algeria, use the global Arabic Numerals, and they were the ones who introduced them to Europe with the advent of Islam into Andalusia, history didn't report to us that Western Arab countries have ever used oriental numbers.

As a result of that, there are two types of numbers in our Arabic writings today and they are different in form. This phenomenon has even included the numbering of the holy Quraanic verses where there are the global Arabic Numerals in the Western Arab countries and the oriental numerals used in the eastern Arab countries.

When the founders of 'Al Diwan for Computer Programmes' started producing computer programmes in Arabic, there were only three brilliant Iraqi young men. Naturally, they used oriental Arabic numbers in their programmes, but after several years these programmes were developed and this coincided with the entry of other companies and establishments into the programme development business, in cooperation with major companies such as Microsoft, Apple and others.

The programmes began to take different dimensions to meet the requirements of nations and their languages. As far as our Arabic Numerals are concerned, two different Arabic programmes were developed, one had the oriental numbers and the other had the global Arabic Numerals. At last, programme developers managed to have both types of numerals in use where users can move from one type to another or vice versa with outstanding ease, by just clicking on a number of icons to get to the desired type, as is the case with choosing the font, type or shape of alphabetic letters which can be changed according to demand.

1- The appearance of the beginning of change in our Arabic numbers

Some Arabic TV stations have undertaken to use our Arabic numbers instead of oriental numerals on their screens. But this didn't take place on an organized strategic or systematic basis. Sometimes you see data in oriental numerals, other times in our Arabic Numerals on the same TV screen. This means the wind of change in numbers has already started blowing, albeit in a disorganized way.

2- Media

Local Arab media are still using the numerical system that is used in their country of origin. As for other international Arab media such as Al Sharq Al Awsat, Al Hayat and Al Quds newspapers and others which are published outside Arab countries, they have started using our Arabic Numerals instead of oriental numbers which are used by their own countries.

Chapter 5

3- Books and Magazines

As far as I know, there has been no move in changing the type of numbers used in books and magazines as has been happening in other media such as newspapers. Probably there are some exceptions in some books such as 'Al Ibadat Al Maliyya Fi Al Islam = Financial Worships in Islam' and 'Al Jihad Al Insani Fi Al Islam = Humanitarian Jihad in Islam'.

4- I have not heard of any signs of change in school syllabi in any country of the countries that still use oriental numbers as education and learning is still dependent on the two types which are the oriental numbers and our Arabic Numerals.

Recommendations of This Study

Now we know that the Arabs were the people who transferred all the knowledge and benefits of previous civilizations to humanity at large, and it was the interests of Arabs themselves in scientific achievements of the Greeks and the Indians that had actually led to the use of the developed arithmetic system in its last Arabic form. Therefore, I recommend the following steps:

1- We must not hold on to cosmetic reasoning and ask which system is more correct. The oriental numbers which are: ١ ٢ ٣ ٤ ٥ ٦ ٧ ٨ ٩ ٠

Or the Arab Western numbers which are: 1 2 3 4 5 6 7 8 9 0

We must know that both types of numerals are Arabic. What is now prevalent in the world is our Arabic Numerals and they are called as such by everyone.

2- We must always remind others in our studies of the important role played by the Arabs and the scientists of the Muslims in human civilization. We must always refer to Al Bairuni, Al Khawarizmi, Al Ya'aqoobi, and Al Iqlidis. Al Bairuni faithfully mentioned in his books that he met the Indians and found them using many groups of numbers and what Arabs took off them was the best they had. Al Bairuni lived in AD 973-1048. But the first Arab writer who wrote about Indian arithmetic was Abu Ja'afar Muhammed Bin Musa Al Khawarizmi. He worked in the office of the Abbasid Caliph Al Maa'moon in the period AD 813-833. The oldest description we have known for the Indian numbers is what we find in Al Ya'aqoobi's book 'Al Tareekh = The History' where he ended his book on the events of Al Iqlidis. He wrote it in Damascus in 341 Hijri (AD 952-953).

3- Two thirds of numbers in the two series, the Indian (or oriental) and our Arabic Numerals, have almost the same form or shape. This is particularly true if we know that the development in some numbers was limited to the divergence of the angle or on a reverse bend, or on a lengthening or omitting of some of their constituent parts as happened in the numbers: 1 2 3 4 5 6 7 8 9 0.

4- We must emphasize that types, the Western and Oriental numerals, are Arabic after some amendments were made on the Indian shapes. This is regarded as an invention of the Arabic civilization from one point of view. Conversely, we must also emphasize the examples the Arabs set and their positive role and contribution to science in their use of numbers in different arithmetic calculations and for setting a value for 'zero' even though it was used by the Greeks and the Indians before them.

Finally, the time is right to reclaim Arabic Numerals for the nation

Requirements for bringing back our Arabic Numerals which are now 'immigrants' across the world:

1- The Arab League should commission an initial study and an explanatory statement and prepare it as a project to be given to Arab governments to be ratified in order to start applying the details of using our Arabic Numerals to replace the oriental numbers which are now used in most Arab countries. The change must take place over a period that must not exceed three years, or five years as a maximum.

2- Ministries of education, planning, information and culture in the Arab world must form separate committees which should give their own recommendations, after which, representatives of these committees must convene in a large comprehensive meeting to approve the last form for the ways and means of effecting the change and the timetable for implementing it.

3- If this is not possible through the Arab League, every country in the Arab Orient should start using our Arabic Numerals by way of adopting these numbers in school syllabi and making their use mandatory in the media and publishing houses.

4- Let us make this change in numbers a scientific and cultural revolution, through which the energies and abilities of our nations in scientific advancements are employed to the maximum, especially in computer sciences, programming and organization. We must open up opportunities for individuals and the private sector so that it can play its role at work and participate in the great operation for change in numbers that have been fluctuating between two types and shapes of numbers.

(And say (unto them): Act! Allah will behold your actions, and (so will) His messenger and the believers, and ye will be brought back to the Knower of the Invisible and the Visible, and He will tell you what ye used to do.)- Soorat At Tawba, verse 105, Holy Quraan.

God is the guarantor of all success.

Sources and Footnotes

1Joy, RR: Shape and Number, London: Macmillan: Education. 1976, P.10.

Abdul Hameed Lutfi and Ahmed Abul Abbas: Tareekh Ar Riyadhiyyat (The History of Mathematics) - Cairo, American University Press, 1957, page 7.

Abdul Hameed Lutfi, the previous source, page 29.

Joy, RR: Shape and Number 1P11.

Joy, RR: Shape and Number.

Joy, RR: Shape and Number.

Ibn An-Nadeem, Muhammed Bin Is-haq: AL Fihrast (The Index), Beirut, Darul Ma'arifa (Publishing House), 1978, Page: 28.

Abdulla Tuhtaah: Is-ham Ulama'a Al Islam fi Ar Riyadhiyyat (The Contribution of the Scholars of Islam in Mathematics). Aalam Al Fikir (Publishing House), (Kuwait), Volume 11, Issue 1, April-June 1980, pages: 283-312.

Abdul Hameed Lutfi, the previous source, page 24. For the use of digits and numbers, you can also look into the following:

- Da'erat Al Ma'arif Al Islamiyya (The Office of Islamic Knowledge), the subject of arithmetic.

- Al Iqleedis, Abul Hassan Ahmed Bin Ibrahim, Al Fusool Fi Al Hisab Al Hindi (The Chapters in Indian Arithmetic), Page: 341 / Edited by Ahmed Sa'eedan, Amman Jordan: The Jordanian Committee for Arabization, Publishing and Translation, 1973.

- Detreesh, Albiar,: Dawr Al Arab Fi Tatawwur Al Uloom Al Tabi'eyya (The Role of the Arabs in the Development of Natural Sciences) / Al Lisan Al Arabi (Rabat), Issue 2, January 1996, Page 96-105.

- The Numbers' Site: www.alargam.com

أرقامنا العربية

عبد الصاحب الشاكري

أرقامنا العربية

تأليـف

عبد الصاحب الشاكري

الناشر

T.C.P.H. Ltd

(دار النشر والاستشارات التكنولوجية)

تأسست سنة 1982

www.islamictourism.com

www.iraqicharities.org

shakiry@tcph.org

مسجلة في بريطانيا

رقم التسجيل 1645411

حقوق الطبع والإخراج الفني محفوظة للناشر

الطبعة الأولى: 1430 هـ - 2009 م

الفهرس

محطات في حياة الشاكري

1931	ولد في العراق وترعرع بمدينة النجف الأشرف، وولج التعليم الديني بها.
1942	شرع بالعمل برعاية أخيه جواد وخلالها واصل تعليم نفسه.
1947-1948	أقام في لبنان لمدة عشرين شهرا، حيث فتحت أمامه آفاق كثيرة.
1949	دخل عالم التجارة والصناعة حيث أسس مع أخويه جواد وحسين شركة دجلة لصناعة الأحذية.
1955	التحق بألمانيا للمشاركة في ورشة تكوينية في علوم الكيمياء وتقنيات المطاط، وشارك في عدة معارض أوربية متخصصة.
1958	شارك في عدة ورشات تكوينية من طرف معامل سفيت لصناعة الأحذية والمطاط (باتا سابقاً) في تشيكوسلوفاكيا وسافر منها إلى ألمانيا وفرنسا وإيطاليا.
1959	مكث في فرانكفورت عشرة أشهر، للمشاركة في عدة ورشات تكوينية في التسيير والإنتاج، حساب كلف الساعات الإنتاجية، أنظمة الكمبيوتر على أجهزة IBM، ثم إلتحاقه بمعهد بيرلت شوله في فرانكفورت لتعليم اللغة الألمانية.
1962	التحق بأول دورة دراسية للإدارة العليا ببغداد تحت إشراف الدكتور حسن سلمان: رئيس جهاز التنمية الصناعية.
1963-1964	إشترى وسيّر شركة داما بألمانيا والمتخصّصة في تسويق وصيانة آلات غسيل الملابس (ميتاك) الأمريكية تدار بالعملة والتي تدخل أوروبا لأول مرة.
1965	شارك في مؤتمر العمل الدولي بجنيف.
1966	- أسّس شركة رافد لصناعة الأحذية وفتح لها أكثر من عشرين فرعاً لتسويق منتجاتها ثم أسس الشركات أدناه.
	- شركة الضياء لمنتجات اللدائن لتصنيع الصموغ والأصباغ.
	- الشركة المتحدة لمنتجات اللدائن ذ.م.م لتصنيع قوالب الأحذية.
	- شركة التمساح لإنتاج الشرائط والأحزمة ذ.م.م، وقد تجاوز عدد العاملين بها 600 إدارياً وعاملاً.
1980	- إنتقل إلى بريطانيا للإقامة بها إلى يومنا هذا.
1983	- أسس شركة T.C.P.H. Ltd. للنشر والتوزيع التي أصدرت:
	- مجلة «الحذاء» الدولية التي تخصّ مواضيع الجلود والأحذية.
	- مجلة «الرداء» الدوليّة التي تخص الغزل والنسيج والملابس.
	- أسس شركة «رافد شو» لصناعة الأحذية.

محطات في حياة الشاكري

- تمكّن من تسجيل اختراع في أوروبا لتصنيع الحذاء (حسب الطلب والقياس خلال ساعة).

1986 - ساهم في شركة لصناعة البسكويت بالمغرب، ثم صار المالك الوحيد لها.

1999 - نشر أول كتاب له بعنوان العبادات المالية في الإسلام.

2001 - أصدر مجلة ثالثة بعنوان السياحة الإسلامية ولا تزال تصدر من لندن لخمس لغات (عربية - فرنسية - إنجليزية - ألمانية - إسبانية) وموقعها الإلكتروني www.islamictourism.com وأغنى كل عدد منها بمقال تحت عنوان آفاق السياحة الإسلامية.

2002 - نشر كتابه الثاني بعنوان الجهاد الإنساني في الإسلام.

2005 - أسّس مبرة الشاكري للتكافل الاجتماعي الخيري بالعراق وهي ترعى أكثر 600 يتيماً.

- أسّس رابطة المبرات العراقية بلندن وموقعها الألكتروني:

www.iraqicharities.org

2007 - أصدر كتابه الثالث آفاق السياحة ويتناول مجمل مقالاته في مجلة السياحة الإسلامية لغاية العدد (27).

- طيلة الفترة ولغاية 2008 لم ينضب عطاؤه حيث واصل بإغناء مجلة «السياحة الإسلامية» بمقالاته المتسلسلة تحت عنوان (آفاق السياحة) في كل عدد.

- وكذلك أغنى الموقع الإلكتروني لرابطة المبرّات العراقية برسائله الأسبوعية التي تتناول مواضيع البناء العلمي من تكوين وتسيير المبرات ونشر ثقافة البرّ والإحسان.

- ساهم في العشرات من الندوات الثقافية والمؤتمرات العلمية والمعارض المتنوعة.

2008 - أصدر كتابه الرابع: آفاق إسلامية للسياحة من أجل السلام العالمي، باللغة العربية.

- أصدر كتابه الرابع: آفاق إسلامية للسياحة من أجل السلام العالمي، باللغة الإنكليزية.

❖ سيصدر له قريباً: كتاب آفاق الصناعة.

تقديم

أرقامنا العربية في ربوع الحضارات

لا يختلف إثنان في التأكيد على حقيقة إنبثاق الحضارة من أرض الرافدين وما حولها من إمتدادات؛ فوجدت الخليقة موقعها المتشعّب والمتطوّر بكياناتها الإجتماعية والحضرية محاطة ما يعرف اليوم بالجزيرة العربية وأرض الرافدين. تلك الارض الطيبة التي انبثق من خلالها النور المحمدي ليشعّ على بقاع العالم بنوره وعلمه وبقائه كبقاء الأزل الشمسي والحساب والعقاب. ومما لا شك فيه؛ إن خليقة تنبثق منها حضارة وتنبثق من تلك الحضارة حضارات لا بدّ أن يكون لوجودها لغة إتصالية ولغة وصفية؛ وبالتالي كانت لغة الأرقام باعتقادنا هي أول لغة استعملها الخلق لكونها وصفية للأشياء وإحتوائها. ناهيك إنّ جسم الإنسان له من المتفرّعات العددية بالأصابع والأضلع والرجلين وغيرها من أعضائه مساراً نحو تحديد ومعرفة لغة الأرقام لتوصيف الأشياء بعددها لا بكيانها. وهذا ما يعطينا إستنتاجاً إن الأرقام كان لها الدور الأكبر في البقاء والتطور والانفتاح على العلم والعلوم وإستمرارية البقاء ليوم الحساب. حتى الكون الذي نحن فيه يصوره الله وما يحويه من أقمار وشمس انهم بحسبان.

حتى إن الخالق الأوحد في وصفه للوجود والبقاء والموت والتوحيد نرى الأرقام متداخلة في عنفوانها للوصف التقديري والوصف التقيمي؛ فحين يخاطب الله آدم وحواء في كتابه الكريم؛ يخاطبهما بلغة الأرقام وحين يطلب من الملائكة أسماء الخلق الجديد يخاطبهما بوصف رقمي؛ وحين نقول أثناء بداية الخلق بوصف رقمي وبلغة عربية ليس إدراجاً إنشائياً منا بقدر ما قال عنه نبي الأمة الكريم «أُحب العرب لثلاث؛ لاني عربي ولأن القرآن عربي ولأن لغة أهل الجنة العربية» أي إن مخاطبة آدم وحواء بلغة عربية كانت وصفية الأرقام؛ «... وَلاَ تَقْرَبَا هَذِهِ الشَّجَرَةَ...» الآية 19 الأعراف؛ وحين يخاطب الشيطان «قَالَ إِنَّكَ مِنَ الْمُنظَرِينَ» الآية 15 الأعراف وحين يخاطب الملائكة يجيبون «قَالُوا سُبْحَانَكَ لاَ عِلمَ لَنَا إِلاَّ مَا عَلَّمْتَنَا إِنَّكَ أَنتَ الْعَلِيمُ الْحَكِيمُ» الآية 32 البقرة؛ وحين يصف الأرض والسموات يصفها بالأرقام الوصفية؛ إلا إنه حين يتحدث عن الوجود والكون بستة أيام؛ أي برقم وجودي؟

تقديم

هذه الإلمامة البسيطة نريد منها أن نقول أن الصفة الخطابية في اللغة العربية هي لغة وصفية رقمية اختلفت في كيانها عن جميع اللغات الحديثة والسابقة؛ فلا تجد مفرد ومثنى وجمع إلّا في اللغة العربية؛ وما عداها يستعمل المفرد والجمع فقط؛ وبالتالي في حين بدأ الخلق في هذه المنطقة التي حددناها آنفا كان ذلك الخلق قبل إقامته دولة المدينة ودولة الدولة وظهور سرجون الأكدي ليوحدها وينشأ أول إمبراطورية في التاريخ؛ وجدوا إن الأرقام هي اللغة الحقيقية التي لا بدّ أن تسود. ولعل الحضارات وما خلّفته من نفائس في متحف اللوفر بفرنسا هو خير دليل على ذلك. فبمجرد النظر الى أية قطعة مما خلفته حضارة الرافدين نجد إن هناك كتابة وتحتوي تلك الكتابة على أرقام في العديد من أركانها؛ في حين إن الحضارات الأخرى التي جاءت بعدها قلما تجد على نفائسها كتابة أو أرقام. وبالتالي فلغة الأرقام ليست موروث حديث؛ بل موروث مع بدأ الخليقة الربانية؛ وهذا الموروث الرباني علمه الله لخلقه ليكتشف من خلاله أشياء أخرى ترسخ وجود وارتباطه بالأرض والحياة. فحين يمتلك الإنسان مالاً أو أرضاً أو حيواناً؛ في بدأ الخليقة كان توصيفه لما يملك توصيفاً رقمياً بعدده وبالصورة التي يراها مناسبة حين ذاك. ناهيك عن إن الكتاب الكريم يعج في تكوينيه الوصفي للآيات بالأرقام وخاصة حين نبحر مع الكتاب الكريم في إتون الغيب وما لحق من أقوام وتحديد صورة الحساب والعقاب والعمل الصالح والعمل الطالح.

فالحديث عن الأرقام بهذه الصورة؛ يراد منه حصر الحضارات التي تعاملت مع الأرقام وخلقت منها وجوداً يمكن أن ينسب إليها في عتمة الزمن؛ لنخرج من هذا إن الغرب وبعض حدود الشرق لم يكن في عهد بدأ الحضارات لهم أي باع في الإرقام؛ بل ما ورد عنهم كان موروث من الحضارات الأخرى التي دخلتهم إما بالتوسّع أو بالحروب المتكرّرة. وعليه لم يكن في الهند في بدأ الخليقة وجود ولا في الغرب وجود؛ بل إنحصر الوجود الإنساني في بداية الخليقة بكل ما بين جزيرة العرب والرافدين وعلى ضفافهما الذي يصل بعدها الجغرافي إلى مصر غرباً وإلى تركيا الحديثة الآن شمالاً وبعض أطراف اليونان المنبثقة عنها الحضارة الإغريقية. وبالتالي إذا ما أريد للبحوث الأركولوجية التعمق في هذه المسألة والدراسة ستجد إن حضارة الأغريق وهي حضارة مكتسبة وليس موروث متطوّر كالحضارات التي وُلدت في المناطق التي حددناها سلفاً. وهو ما يوصلنا إلى نتيجة إن الإستناج الذي جاء به الأستاذ عبدالصاحب الشاكري في كتابه الذي بين يدينا الموسوم بـ «أرقامنا العربية» هو إستناج صحيح وصائب ولا غبار عليه.

أرقامنا العربية في ربوع الحضارات

أرقامنا العربية؛ الذي أعتبره من النتاجات القيمة التي بما لا يقبل الشك سيكون مهماً في المستقبل القريب والبعيد؛ صور بصورة جميلة وبسياق لغوي سلس وبإسنادات بحثية قيمة التطور العلمي الذي رافق مسيرة العرب والمسلمين؛ ولعل الإحتواء العلمي في فصليه الأول والثاني للإنجازات العربية في مجال الرياضات وفعل الأرقام بالعلوم الأخرى كان إلتفاتة يحتاج إليها الباحث العربي والمسلم؛ خصوصاً في وقت عجت فيه الإنقيادات إلى كل ما هو غربي؛ ونكران كل ما هو إسلامي وعربي. وقد يعارض علينا معترض بقوله ما فائدة الماضي والحديث عنه؛ والواقع الأمم التي بدون تاريخ لا يمكن أن تنهض وتبقى متخلفة. ولعله في أي بحث علمي لا يمكن أن يكون هناك تطور دون الرجوع إلى الأسس التاريخية للعلوم. هذا السرد الواضح والمتواضع الذي جاء به الأستاذ الشاكري فتح أمامنا مداخل كثيرة لإثبات عروبة وأسلمة الأرقام وتطوّر وتقدّم العرب والمسلمين في حينه؛ في حين إن الأمم الأخرى كانت متخلفة تماماً. فالإستفادة الكبيرة التي وجدتها في حديث المؤلف والتي تعتبر بحق فلسفة رقمية جديدة هي ما تحدّث فيه عن دور الدولة العباسية في تطوّر العلوم وخاصة في بناء الساعة. فالساعة حين وضع تقسيماتها الرياضيون حين ذاك؛ اعتبروا إن بدأ الوقت يبدأ من الصفر وعلى ضوئه تم تقسيم الساعات والثواني والدقائق. ولعل هذه الطفرة العلمية في الرياضيات والتي سبقتها بالأرقام وكيفية استعمالاتها هي التي مهدت لإنبثاق علوم عديدة كان لها الأثر الجبار في تطور العلوم الأخرى.

هناك حقيقة وهي إن اللغة العربية هي لغة رقمية رياضية؛ وما الأوزان الشعرية إلاّ مثالاً على ذلك إذا ما عرفنا إن الوزن الشعري يعتمد على الحركة والسكون؛ وهو ما يسمى اليوم بالأرقام الثنائية المتكوّنة من 0 و1. وعليه إن الصفر مهما تعدّدت الطروحات فاننا نميل الى رأي الأستاذ الباحث الشاكري إنه عربي المنشأ وهو مأخوذ من اللغة قبل أن تكون استعمالاته المتعدّدة تغيّر في مفاهيم الهندسة والفيزياء والكيمياء والعلوم الأخرى؛ سواء التي أبدع فيها العرب المسلمون أو التي لم يبدعوا فيها قط. فما جاء به الأستاذ عبدالصاحب الشاكري لا يختلف فيه الباحثون؛ وحتى دعاة الصفر الهندي نراهم حين يستمرون في إثباته يقفون في النهاية عند مفترق طريق فيقولون وهناك نظريات تثبت عروبة الصفر بالنسبة إلى ما تمّ نقله عنه في الدولة العربية في الأندلس؛ وبعضهم يصل إلى أبعد من ذلك فيقول دخل مع الإحتلال الفاطمي لأواسط أوروبا.

تقديم

لقد جال الباحث الأستاذ صاحب الشاكري في أتون كتابة الحروف وكيفية التعامل معها صينياً وفينيقياً وهندياً وغربياً وشرقياً وغيرها من اللغات التي لها حضارات؛ خصوصا وقد وصفنا معظمها بكونها حضارات مقتبسة غير موروثة ومع هذا فلها دلوها في إرساء العلوم وتطويرها. وعليه فالشاكري بنفس بحثي رياضي قدير تمكن من شرح الأشكال والملابسات التي وجدت فيها تلك الارقام وحيثيات كتابة أشكالها وخلص في إستنتاجه إلى عربية الأرقام وهو إستنتاج منطقي رياضي بحت لا بدّ من الإستناد إليه في أي بحث في هذا الموضوع. إذ ربط من خلال هذا الإكتشاف أهمية التطوّر في العلوم الحديثة بالأرقام وما له من تأثير في كيفية بناء منظومة علمية عربية تجعله يسهل دخول التطوّر العلمي من باب الأرقام وكيفية معالجتها كومبيوترياً. وهو صواب في الرأي ولا بدّ من الإنطلاق في فهم هذا الواقع.

إن الصرخة التي اطلقها الباحث في ضرورة اعتماد الأرقام العربية (0؛ 1؛ 2؛ 3؛ ....الخ) هي صرخة حقيقة حريصة على تطوّر العلوم وإسهاماتها بهذه الصورة الجلية؛ وهو كما قال الباحث لا يمكن أن يتم ما لم يكن هناك تبنّي لها من كافة الدول العربية والإسلامية لنعيد الحق لمناصه ونعمل على تطويره وإثباته؛ وسيكون باباً لإرجاع الأسماء العربية الإسلامية العلمية اللامعة لأخذ حقها كالخوارزمي والبيروني وغيرهم الذين نُهب تراثهم وأُسند بأسماء لم يكن لها دور أو معنى لولا سرقتهم حقوق هؤلاء.

ليس غريباً أن يكون هذا البحث من لدن الأخ الأستاذ عبدالصاحب الشاكري لأنه سبق وأن أتحف المكتبة العربية ببحوث ومجلات لم يكن قد إلتفت إليها قبله وأخصّ بالذكر مجلة «الحذاء» ومجلة «الرداء» ومجلة «السياحة الإسلاميّة» والتي لولاه لما تمكّن القارىء الغربي التعرّف على إسهامات العرب والمسلمين؛ لكونه حرص كل الحرص على إصدارها باللغة العربية واللغة الانكليزية. ناهيك عن أنه دأب ومنذ ذلك الحين على نشر نتاجاته في اللغة الإنكليزية وغيرها من اللغات الأوروبية الحديثة بجانب اللغة العربية ليطلع المجتمع الغربي على ما ينتجه العرب والمسلمين من بحوث؛ بارك الله فيك وبانتظار نتاجات أخرى.

د. هيثم غالب الناهي

لندن   1 ديسمبر (كانون الأول) 2008

المقدمة

لـقـد أخـذت تسـاؤلاتي واهـتمـامـاتي حـول الأرقـام تكبـر يومـاً بعد يوم مـنذ بدايـة الثمانينيات من القرن الماضي، وذلك خلال نشري لمجلتي الحذاء والرداء اللتين كانت محتوياتهما تنشر باللغة العربية والإنجليزية، وبما أن اهتماماتهما كانت منصبة على الشؤون العلمية والاقتصادية والمهنية، بصفتهما مجلتان مهنيتان، وكان من طبيعة مثل هذا النشر أن تتطلب جداول وأرقاما، فكنت أشعر عند صدور كل عدد بضيق وألم حيث لا أرى أي مبرر أو مسوغ باستعمال نوعين من الأرقام لاسيما أن الإثنين يعتبران عربيان بالإضافة إلى أن الأرقام الشرقية هي أكثر صعوبة في الكتابة والقراءة واحتمال الأخطاء فيها أكثر، لهذا كله فإن تكرار أو استعمال نوعين من الأرقام، كان في رأيي مضيعة للوقت والجهد ومعرقلا للإبداع الفني والعلمي والمعرفي في التصميم والإخراج وغيرها من المبررات التي تعطي أرقامنا العربية، المميزات والأفضلية على غريمتها الأرقام المشرقية.

وبمرور الأيام أخذت تزداد رغبتي وميلي نحو استعمال أرقامنا العربية، عربية الأصل، غربية عالمية الاستعمال، والتي تستعمل في دول المغرب العربي ومعظم دول العالم وتسمى بالأرقام العربية، بدلاً من استعمال الأرقام المشرقية التي هي بالأصل أرقام هندية:

(للاختصار سوف نطلق إسم، أرقامنا العربية ، على الأولى، والأرقام المشرقية، على الثانية) .

بعد هذا، أخذت أصرّ على العاملين الذين يطبعون نصوص مواضيع المجلتين، وكذلك عند شرائنا لأجهزة الحواسيب (الكومبيوتر) كنت أطلب أن يستعملوا أرقامـنا العربيـة بدلاً من الأرقـام المشرقيـة إلا أن برنامج الكومبيوتر العربي (السوفت وير) المعدّ كان يعمل في ذلك الوقت فقط على الأرقام المشرقية وكانت عملية تغيير الرقم من المشرقية إلى أرقامنا العربية عملية معقدة وتستغرق وقتاً طويلاً حينما يتطلّب الأمر تغيير كل رقم برقم، فتكون النتيجة خليط من الرقمين المشرقي والعربي في النصوص العربية، فظلّ هاجس التغيير يسيطر على فكري كلما أقوم بعمل تحرير أو إصدار مجلة أو كتاب .

وعند إصدار كتابي (العبادات المالية في الإسلام) كان إصراري جلياً على ضرورة تحقيق وتنفيذ ما أعتقده صواباً في جعل أرقامه كلها وحتى أرقام الآيات القرآنية،

أرقاماً عربية، وذلك نتيجة لتواجدي في المغرب، بعدما تأكد لي بأن أرقامنا العربية هي الواعدة للمستقبل.

وها أنا الآن أعود إلى محاولة إصدار هذا الكتاب بعدما تأخّرت عن إنجازه لسنوات عديدة نتيجة انشغالي بنشر مجلة «السياحة الإسلامية» وتأسيس موقع لها.

ثم أخذت فكرة عمل الكتاب حول الأرقام العربية تتجسّد وتتبلور منذ بداية التسعينيات ومنذ ذلك التاريخ كنت أبحث عن مصادر لتساعدني في إخراج بحثي هذا إلى الوجود، حيث قمت بالانتماء إلى عضوية المكتبة البريطانية العامة وهي أكبر مكتبة متطورة في لندن وأخذت بالتحدث في موضوع كتابي هذا مع الأصدقاء إلى أن التقيت بمناسبة سعيدة مع صديق الصبا الأستاذ عبد اللطيف الملح، العضو السابق لجمعية التراث البغدادي الذي وافاه الأجل (رحمه الله) قبل أن تتحقق رغبته في رؤية هذا الكتاب، وكنت قد طرحت عليه موضوع الأرقام، فقال يمكنني أن أبحث لك عن ذلك في رفوف مكتباتنا في العراق ولا بدّ من إيجاد أجوبة للتساؤلات التي لديك في كيفية تطوّر الأرقام وما هي أصلها وفصلها حيث برّ بوعده بعد عدة أشهر وأسعفني بالبحث القيم الذي سيرد في هذا الكتاب والذي يعتبر ركنا مهما من أركان بحثنا هذا فألف شكر له.

الآن بعدما تكاملت عناصر هذا الكتاب من بحوث تاريخية وموجبات للتغيير وقواعد علمية وتكنولوجية وإعطاء الأمثلة في تجارب الشعوب وقادتها في إحداث الثورات التغييرية في الحقول العلمية والثقافية والعمرانية وكل ما يخصّ تطور الإنسان والإنسانية، لا بدّ أن نوجّه نداءنا إلى حكومات بلداننا العربية التي بدأت مؤسساتها الإعلامية والثقافية تتأرجح مابين شكلي الأرقام المشرقية وأرقامنا العربية التي أخذت بها 95٪ من دول العالم.

لقد حان الوقت الآن أن نتخذ خطوات علمية ثورية سريعة من أجل تغيير الأرقام في المناهج الدراسية، وكذلك على مستوى الإعلام والنشر، وبذلك نساير دول العالم ومتطلّبات التكنولوجية الحديثة في ثورة الحواسيب والاتصالات.

حان الوقت لتقوم الدول العربية بمبادرة تغيير وتوحيد أرقام أمتنا العربية وذلك بالدعوة إلى تغيير الأرقام المشرقية بالأرقام العربية الأصل والمتداولة عالمياً، في كافة الدول العربية التي تستعمل الرقم الشرقي وتنفيذ ذلك بشكل علمي منظم كما

هو الحال اليوم في أوروبا التي بدأت بتوحيد عملة خمسة وعشرين دولة إلى عملة موحّدة وإسمها (اليورو)، فهل استرجاع ما أخذ منّا من شكل الأرقام التي تسمى باسمنا أي أرقامنا العربية ووضعها محل الأرقام المشرقية التي لم تعد تصلح مع علوم التكنولوجيا الحديثة هي مسألة مستحيلة أو صعبة أو معقدة؟ الجواب حتماً: (لا)، إنها عملية سهلة بمنتهى السهولة بعدما مكّنت أجهزة الكمبيوتر والبرامج المعدّة لها من ذلك فإن اليوم باستطاعة العاملين على أجهزة الحاسوب (الكومبيوتر) القيام بالضغط على بعض الأزرار لتغيير الأرقام من شكل لآخر في النص العربي بكامله أو كافة النصوص المطبوعة على الكومبيوتر مهما كانت أشكالها أو أنواعها.

في ختام مقدمتي هذه لا بدّ لي من أن أتقدّم بالشكر والتقدير لكل الذين ساعدوني في البحث والمراجعة وتبويب نصوص هذا الكتاب وترجمته وكل الأخوة والأخوات اللذين ساهموا في الطبع والترتيب وعملوا على انجازه.

فلنخض أسفار كتابنا هذا: (أرقامنا العربية).

والله ولي التوفيق.

عبد الصاحب الشاكري

الفصل الأول

الرياضيات عند العرب المسلمين

الرياضيات

المعروف أن المسلمين بنوا معارفهم في الرياضيات على أساس من علوم اليونان والهنود ثم تقدموا بهذه العلوم وخطوا بها خطوات نحو الأمام حتى ظهر منهم في المشرق علماء مبرزون في العلوم الرياضية مثل الخوارزمي (ت 835-844 م) وثابت ابن قرة (ت 901 م) والبتاني (ت 926 م) والخازن البصري (ولد حوالي 960 م) وعمر ابن إبراهيم الخيام (ت 1132 م). أما في المغرب الإسلامي فقد ظهر مسلمة المجريطي إمام الرياضيين بالأندلس (1007 م) والذي كان من تلامذة ابن السمح (ت 1034 م) وابن الصفار والكرماني وغيرهم.

وتقدّم المسلمون بالحساب خطوات واسعة فأضافوا إلى معلومات اليونان كثيراً من النظريات التي لم تعرفها أوربا من قبل، كما علّموا الأوروبيين نظام الأعداد الهندية الذي يمثّل ثورة شاملة في علم الحساب. ويتضح لنا تسهيل هذا النظام العددي للعمليات الحسابية إذا قارنا بينه وبين النظام العددي الروماني. فنظام الأعداد الجديد الذي عرفته أوروبا عن العرب، يمكن فيه أن تتغيّر قيمة الواحد حسب وضعه في خانة الآحاد أو العشرات أو الآلاف أو الملايين في حين أن قيمة الرقم لا تتغيّر في النظام الروماني بتغيير خانته، فالرقم خمسة (5) مثلاً لا يمكن أن يعني خمسين أو خمسمائة أو خمسة آلاف. وهكذا إذا أردنا أن نكتب عددا مثل 27 بالأرقام اللاتينية - التي لم تعرف أوربا غيرها في العصور الوسطى - فإنه يكتب على هذا الوضع. XXVII ونستطيع أن نتصوّر مدى التعقيد الذي يصيب العمليات الحسابية من جمع وطرح وضرب وقسمة عند إستخدام هذا النظام العددي الروماني، فما بالنا بالأعداد الكبيرة التي تعبّر عن الآلاف والملايين أو الجداول الرياضية والمعادلات.

حقيقة أن الأعداد الجديدة المستخدمة حالياً في الغرب ليست من اختراع الغرب، إذ المرجّح أنها هندية الأصل، كما أشار العرب أنفسهم وكما يتضح من طريقة كتابتها من اليسار إلى اليمين، ولكن يكفي العرب فضلاً أنهم أوصلوا هذه الطريقة الجديدة إلى أوروبا ورحموا الأوروبيين من تعقيد النظام العددي الروماني العقيم، وبذلك سهلوا العمليات الحسابية وساعدوا على تقدّم الرياضيات .

وقد كتب البيروني رسالة هامة في الأعداد ونسبها أسماها «راشيكات الهند» كما شرح اليعقوبي في تاريخه نظام الأعداد الجديد الذي أخذه العرب عن الهنود فقال : «.... ووضع الأحرف الهندية التسعة التي تخرّج منها جميع الحسابات الذي لا يدرك معرفتها، وهي (1,2,3,4,5,6,7,8,9) فالأولى منها واحد وعشرة ومائة وهو ألف ومائة ألف وهو ألف ألف ... وعلى هذا الحساب يجري التسعة أحرف فصاعداً. غير أن بيت الواحد معروف من العشرة وكذلك بيت العشرة معروف من المائة وكذلك بيت كل بيت، وإذا خلا بيت منها يجعل فيها الصفر ويكون الصفر دائرة صغيرة.».

وهنا نجد اليعقوبي يشير إلى رمز حسابي جديد هو الصفر الذي يعتبر من أخطر المبادئ التي اهتدى إليها العقل البشري في الرياضيات. ولم يعرف الغرب إستعمال الصفر إلّا عن طريق العرب في القرن الثاني عشر، حتى قال المؤرخ أير Eyre إن فكرة الصفر تعتبر من أعظم الهدايا العلمية التي قدّمها المسلمون إلى غرب أوروبا. وكان العرب قد استخدموا لفظ (صفر) للدلالة على (لاشيء) منذ العصر الجاهلي، كما يبدو في البيت التالي الذي جاء في قصيدة لحاتم.

ترى إن هلكت لم يك ضرني.... وإن يدي مما بخلت به صفر

وفي القرن الثامن الميلادي إستخدم المسلمون الصفر في الحساب، فرسموه على هيئة حلقة. كما ذكر اليعقوبي في النص السابق. وكذلك ذكر محمد بن أحمد في (مفاتيح العلوم) أنه إذا لم يظهر في العمليات الحسابية رقم مكان العشرات وجب أن توضع دائرة صغير «لمساواة الصفوف» ثم شرح الخوارزمي كيفية إستعمال الأعداد الجديدة، بما فيها الصفر، في بحث له ترجمه الأوروبيون إلى اللاتينية في الربع الأول من القرن الثاني عشر تحت إسم: (Algoritmi de Numero Indorum) أي الخوارزمي عن أرقام الهنود. هكذا اشتقّ اللفظ الأوروبي Chiffre عن (صفر) وهو يعني أيضاً في اللغات الأوروبية (لا شيء أو عديم القيمة)، فاستخدم مارتن لوثر هذا اللفظ للتعبير عن ضعف الأساقفة أمام البابا فقال أنهم كالأصفار. وفي القرن السادس عشر إستخدم اللفظ الأوروبي السابق Chiffer للدلالة على الكتابة الغامضة أو الشفرة، في حين استخدم لفظ Zero، بمعنى لا شيء.

وهكذا تلقى غرب أوربا نظام الأعداد الجديد مقرونا باسم الخوارزمي وسرعان ما حور إسم الخوارزمي في اللغة اللاتينية – وهو Algoritmi – إلى Algorismus ثم اختصر بعد ذلك إلى Augrim، حتى أصبح هذا اللفظ الأخير علماً لنظام الأعداد العشري الجديد. ويدلّ كل ذلك على أن الغربيين تعلّموا الحساب الحديث عن كتاب الخوارزمي السابق، وعن الكتب الأخرى التي أخذت عنه، مثل كتاب Carmen de Algorisme الذي وضعه السكندردي فيلادي Alexandre de Villa حوالي سنة 1220م. وكتاب Algorismus Vulgaris الذي وضعه حنا الهالفكسي John of Halifax حوالي سنة 1250م. وكل من هذين الكتابين الأخيرين مبني إلى حد كبير على كتاب محمد بن موسى الخوارزمي في الحساب، كما أن كلاهما استمرا مرجعاً لتلقين الحساب في غرب أوروبا عدة قرون. وما زالت اللغة الإنكليزية حتى اليوم تستخدم لفظ الجورزم Algorithm وهو تحريف لإسم الخوارزمي – للتعبير عن الطريقة الوضعية في حل المسائل.

ولم يقتصر فضل العرب على أوروبا في ميدان الرياضيات على علم الحساب وإنما امتدّ إلى بقية العلوم، وعلى رأسها علم الجبر الذي لا يزال محتفظاً بإسمه العربي في كافة اللغات الأوروبية (Algebra, Algebre)، بعد أن أخذه الأوروبيون عن العرب وإذا كان بعض الباحثين يميل إلى الاعتقاد بأن العرب ليسوا هم الذين وضعوا أصول علم الجبر، وأن هذه الأصول عرفت منذ أيام ديوفانتوس Diophantus وهو عالم يوناني عاش في القرن الثالث، إلا أنه يكفي العرب فخراً أنهم اكتشفوا أصول علم الجبر وأضافوا إليها وحوّلوها تحويلاً تاماً، وخلقوا منها علماً حقيقياً بمعنى الكلمة، ثم طبّقوا هذا على الهندسة وقد بلغ من اهتمام العرب بعلم الجبر أن الخليفة المأمون كلّف محمد بن موسى الخوارزمي بوضع كتاب في هذا العِلم، وهو الكتاب الذي نقله إلى اللاتينية روبرت الشستر Robert of Chester سنة 1145 م، وبذلك قدّم العرب علماً جديداً إلى أوروبا، إذ ظلّ هذا الكتاب مستعملاً في المدارس والجامعات الأوروبية حتى القرن السادس عشر. ومن علماء العرب الذين كتبوا في الجبر أيضاً أبو بكر محمد بن الكرخي المتوفى بين سنتي 1019-1020 م، ويعتبر من أكبر علماء العرب الذين شهدتهم بغداد على عهد أبي غالب محمد بن خلف الملقب فخر المُلك وزير بهاء الدين عضد الدولة بن بوية. ومن أجله صنّف الكرخي كتابين (الفخري في الجبر والمقابلة) وكتاب

(الكايخ في الحساب). والكتاب الأول أكثر أهمية، ويلي في أهميته الكتاب الذي وضعه عمر بن إبراهيم الخيام (1045,1123 م) في علم الجبر.

أما في الهندسة وعلم المثلثات فقد ترجم العرب كتاب إقليدس في الهندسة، وهي الترجمة العربية التي نقلها الأوروبيون إلى اللاتينية في القرن الثاني عشر. كذلك ترجم الكوسي (بتاريخ 1274 م) كتاب المعطيات لإقليدس، وهو في هندسة الأشكال الكروية، ولكن العرب لم يقتصروا على معلومات اليونان في الهندسة وحساب المثلثات، وإنما جددوا وأضافوا إضافات جديدة لم تعرف من قبلهم، فهم الذين أدخلوا المماس إلى علم حساب المثلثات، وكان لهذه الخطوة أهمية عظمى في الرياضيات، حتى اعتبرها علماء الرياضات ثورة علمية خطيرة. كذلك أقام العرب الجيوب مقام الأوتار، وحلّوا المعادلات المكعّبة، وتعمّقوا في أبحاث المخروطات، ولا شك في أن هذه المعلومات الجديدة هي التي جعلت العلوم الرياضية تتبوّأ أهميتها في الحياة. ومن أبرز العلماء المسلمين الذين كتبوا في الهندسة وحساب المثلثات الخوارزمي، وثابت بن قرة، والبتاني، والخازن البصري، وابن الهيثم، والبيروني وارتقى أبو عبد الله البتاني (850-939 م) المعروف عند الأوربيين باسم Albategnus بعلم حساب المثلثات إلى أبعد مبادئه التي كان عليه أيام بكليوس السكندري، وذلك حين استبدل المثلّثات بالمربّعات في حلّ المسائل واستبدل جيب الزاوية بالقوس وهو الذي صاغ حساب المثلثات بالنسب بالصورة التي نستخدمها الآن. أما رسالة ابن الهيثم في حساب المثلثات فتسمى (شكل بني موسى) وهو يعلّل هذه التسمية (بأن الأشكال التي قدمها بنو موسى ببراهين كتاب المخروطات، هو الشكل الأخير من مقدماتهم). أمّا البيروني فكتب رسالة في استخراج الأوتار في الدائرة. ومعظم هذه المؤلّفات العربية قام الأوربيون بترجمتها إلى اللاتينية منذ القرن الثاني عشر، ونخصّ بالذكر أديلارد الباثي الذي ترجم جداول حساب المثلثات للخوارزمي سنة 1162م، كما ترجم غيرها من مؤلّفات الهندسة.

أما معلومات العرب في الميكانيكا فهي واسعة وعظيمة، تدل عليها بقايا آلاتهم ووصفهم لها في الكتب. وهنا أيضاً إهتم العرب بترجمة كتابات اليونان، واستمرّ هذا الإهتمام حتى القرن الثالث عشر عندما نجد الطوسي يترجم كتاب الكرة المتحركة (لاوطولوقس Utolycus)، ولكن العرب زادوا على هذه المعلومات، حتى يرى بعض العلماء الأوربيين أنهم اخترعوا رقاص الساعة واستعملوا البندول في

قياس الوقت. ومعنى ذلك أنهم عرفوا الساعات ذات الأثقال التي تختلف كثيرا عن الساعات المائية، كما يتضح من وصف ساعة المسجد الأموي التي ورد ذكرها في المراجع.

وخلاصة القول إن العرب قطعوا شوطاً بعيداً في الرياضيات، فاستفادت أوروبا منهم فائدة عظيمة في هذا الميدان. وإن المتأمّل في كتاب من كتب العرب الرياضية يأخذه العجب بما وصل إليه رياضيو العرب من اتساع المعرفة ودقة البحث. فهذا الخوارزمي يتعرض لشرح المعادلات ذات الحدين والثلاثة حدود شرحاً علمياً وافياً، ثم يتناول الجذور، وكيفية استخراج مساحة الأشكال الهندسية المختلفة كالمربع والمثلث والمعين والدائرة. وبعد ذلك ينتقل إلى مسائل معقدة ويحدد طرق حلها في دقة ومهارة تثير الدهشة...

الفصل الثاني

دور علماء العرب والمسلمين في تطوير الشكل النهائي
وإستخدامات أرقامنا العربية التي شاع إستخدامها
في كل ركن من أركان المعمورة

أصبح موضوع استخدام الأرقام العربية من الموضوعات التي تحتاج إلى إبراز دور علماء العرب المسلمين في تطوير هذه الأرقام وأثر ذلك في الحضارة الإنسانية:

وتدور أحيانا بين أوساط المثقفين تساؤلات حول ما هو شكل الأرقام العربية، هل هي الأرقام المشرقية الحالية: ٠٩٨٧٦٥٤٣٢١

أم الأرقام العربية المستخدمة في أغلب دول العالم وبعض دول المغرب العربي: 0 9 8 7 6 5 4 3 2 1

ولعلّ مصدر هذا التساؤل يدفعنا إلى دراسة نستجلى بها دور العرب في استخدام الأرقام، ونؤكد على الدور الحضاري لعلماء العرب المسلمين في بلورة أرقامنا العربية.

ومن أجل هذه لابد من تقسيم هذه الدراسة إلى الأقسام التالية:
- إستخدام الأرقام عبر العصور.
- إستخدام الأرقام عند العرب.
- توصيات الدارسة.

إستخدام الأرقام عبر العصور

الحضارة العربية الإسلامية، حضارة شأنها شأن كل الحضارات تتأثر بما سبقها من حضارات، وتترك بصماتها على ما يلحقها من حضارات.

والعرب يعترفون بفضل الحضارات السابقة، لهذا فإن الحضارة العربية الإسلامية لم تكن وليدة الصدفة، أو دون ترتيب سابق.

وإن للرياضيات، ولنقل الحساب وبالتالي الأرقام بصفة محدّدة، الخاص بالحضارات السابقة، أثر واضح في الحضارة العربية الإسلامية.

وسوف أقدم شكل هذه الأرقام عبر العصور عند المصريين القدماء والبابليين، والصينيين، والإغريقيين والرومانيين والهنود.

1 - نظام العدد المصري القديم

استخدم المصريون القدماء منذ أكثر من 5000 سنة، رموزاً للأعداد: الواحد، العشرة، المائة، الألف، العشرة آلاف، المائة ألف والمليون. ولم يكن لديهم رمز للصفر، كما أن نظامهم العددي لم يكن يعتمد على فكرة القيمة المكانية (أو الخانة آحاد - عشرات...إلخ) بل إن الرمز كان يكرر كثيراً ربما على عدد نراه الآن بسيطاً - بعد إبتكار النظام العشري ورمز الصفر وفكرة الخانة - وقد كانت اللغة الهيروغليفية هي لغة قدماء المصريين، حيث كانت رموز الأعداد الهيروغليفية تكتب كما بالشكل أدناه:

الأرقام الهيروغليفية

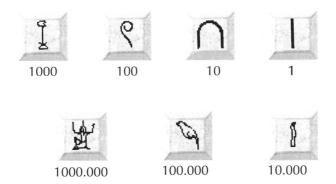

مثال عددي

1.246.323

لقد أجمع كل الكتّاب الإغريق على أسبقية مصر في كشف العلوم الرياضية، فقد ذكر أفلاطون أن الإله توت بمصر كان مخترعاً لفنون عدة منها الحساب والهندسة والفلك، وقال أرسطو أن مولد الرياضيات بمصر لأن طبقة الكهنة لديها من الفراغ ما يسمح بدراستها، واستنتج هيرودوت بأن الهندسة بدأت بمصر ثم نقلت إلى الإغريق.

وأول مرجع كما يذكر لنا علماء تاريخ الرياضيات، لدى المصريين القدماء في مجال الرياضيات هو قرطاس أحس، وقد عثر عليه ريند Rhind سنة 1858 وترجمة ايزنلور Eisenlohr سنة 1877 وهذب الترجمة بيت Peet سنة 1923، وهذا القرطاس من عهد الأسرة الثانية عشرة (1849/1801 ق.م) ويعتقد برش Birch أن ما ورد به من معلومات يرجع إلى سنة 3400 ق.م وقد أسماه مؤلّفه (إرشادات للحصول على معرفة كل الأشياء القائمة).

ويحتوي الكتاب على خمسة أبواب، وفيه 87 مسألة:

الباب الأول: العد وكتابة الأرقام.

الباب الثاني: القواعد الأربعة .

الباب الثالث: الكسور.

الباب الرابع: المربع والجذر التربيعي وحل معادلات الدرجة الأولى والمتواليات.

الباب الخامس: الهندسة.

2 – الأعداد عند شعوب ما بين النهرين

عُثر، في أماكن متفرقة، على أختام قديمة، تدلّ على وجود علاقات تجارية بين السومريين – أقدم شعوب بلاد ما بين النهرين – ومصر والهند كما عُثر أيضاً على كثير من الألواح الطينية، وعليها كتابات سومرية، تكشف عن حياة تجارية نشطة، فيها عقود يشهد عليها شهود، ووثائق تكشف عن أساليب القروض، وفوائدها، التي تتراوح بين 25 % إلى 33 % في السنة. ويبدو أن السومريين قد أخذوا علوم الحساب عن المصريين، أو العكس، ولكنهم على أية حال، توصلوا إلى اكتشاف الأرقام، في حدود عام 3700 ق.م، في تل حرمل بالعراق، ومما ورد، في هذا الشأن، نص عن رجل يسمى آشور بانيبال يذكر فيه أنه تعلّم كيفية إيجاد العوامل المشتركة، وإجراء العمليات الحسابية. ونصٌّ آخر، بعنوان «قضايا علمية»، يتحدث عن أساليب تدريس الرياضيات، في المدارس، وجداول الضرب.

وجاء البابليون، بعد السومريين، وورثوا عنهم معرفة الأعداد، في حوالي 2400 ق.م، ثم الآشوريون كذلك. وقد أولت شعوب ما بين النهرين الأعداد عناية بالغة،

وتوصلوا إلى وضع عدد من القواعد الحسابية، مثيرة للإعجاب. وكتبوا الأعداد على أقراص من الفخار، باستخدام آلات حادة، في خط أفقي من اليمين إلى اليسار، واستخدموا علامات تدلّ على الطرح، فمثلاً العدد 19 يكتبونه 20 مطروحاً منها واحد، كما فعل الرومان بعد ذلك.

وكانت الرموز التي استخدموها تُعرف بالأشكال المسمارية، فجعلوا رمز العدد «واحد» على شكل مسمار قائم، يتكرر من الواحد إلى التسعة، أما العشرة فجعلوها على الشكل ⟨ أما الأحد عشر، فهي العشرة معها علامة المسمار «واحد» إلى يسارها، أما المائة فجعلوها على شكل ◄ أي خطين، أحدهما عمودي، والآخر أفقي عن يمينه. أما الألف، فكان يُصوَّر باعتباره عشر ◄ مئات فإذا زيدت عشرة على اليسار، كان العدد عشرة آلاف وهكذا. وكانت أسماء الأعداد، من واحد إلى خمسة، موافقة لأسماء أصابع اليد الواحدة، كالتالي:

1 = آش
2 = من
3 = إش
4 = لمو
5 = أي أويا

ثم يضيفون «أي» إلى الأرقام الأولى، لتعني زيادة خمسة، فأصبحت:

6 = ياش (آي آش)
7 = أي من
8 = أيشو (آي شو)
9 = ألمو (أي لمو)

أما العشرة، فاسمها (أو)، وضعفها العشرون هو نش، ومن العشرة ومركباتها جاءت:

30 = أو شو (أي 3 عشرات)
40 = نش من (أي 2 × 20)
50 = نينو (نيني أو) أي (2 × 20 + 10)

وهكذا توصل السومريون، ومن بعدهم، إلى النظام العشري، وابتكروا النظام
الستيني، واتخذوه وحدة عددية، عندما رأوا أن محيط الدائرة ينقسم إلى ستة أوتار
متساوية، كل وتر منها يساوي نصف قطر الدائرة، وقد فطنوا لذلك لمّا رأوا بيوت
النحل سداسية الأشكال. ثم لاحظوا أن الدائرة تنقسم إلى ستة مثلثات متساوية
الأضلاع، قياس كل زاوية فيها ستون درجة، ثم وافق تقسيمهم هذا تقسيم السنة
موافقة عجيبة: 6 × 60 = 360 يوماً.

المصدر: www.alargam.com

3 - الأعداد في الصين

كان للصينيين الفضل في وضع أساس القيمة المحلية للرقم، أو الخانات، فمهدوا
للهنود كشف الأرقام الهندية التي نستخدمها الآن، وفيما يلي نوضح شكل الأرقام
الصينية:

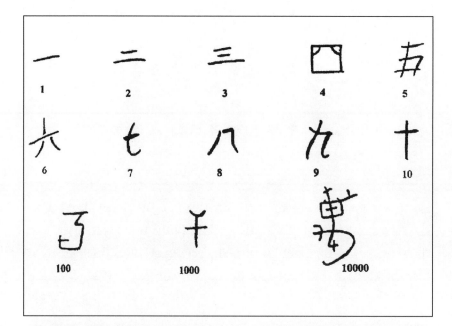

يتكوّن نظام رموز الترقيم الصيني من الرموز المستخدمة في اللغة الصينية لكتابة الأرقام. هذه الرموز تمثل الأرقام من الصفر وحتى تسعة وهناك رموز أخرى تمثل أرقاما أكبر كالعشرات والمئات والآلاف وهكذا. وهناك طاقمان من الرموز المستخدمة في الترقيم الصيني: الأول للإستخدام اليومي في الكتابة والثاني للإستخدام في السياقات التجارية أو الماليه والمعروفة في الصين بمصطلح داسيا (لاحظ الجدول أدناه). اليوم نظام ترميز الأرقام الصينية يستخدم نفس الطريقة التي يتم بها تركيب الكلمات هجائياً والدالة على الأرقام باللغة الإنكليزية.

التقليدي (يستخدم في هونغ كونك وتايوان)

المبسط (يستخدم في الصين)

التقليدي الرسمي (داسيا) يستخدم في هونغ كونك وتايوان

المبسط الرسمي (داسيا) يستخدم في الصين

	0	1	2	3	4	5	6	7	8	9	10	100	1000
التقليدي(يستخدم في هونغ كونك وتايوان)	零	一	二	三	四	五	六	七	八	九	十	百	千
المبسط(يستخدم في الصين)	零	一	二	三	四	五	六	七	八	九	十	百	千
التقليدي الرسمي(داسيا)يستخدم في هونغ كونك وتايوان	零	壹	貳	參	肆	伍	陸	柒	捌	玖	拾	佰	仟
المبسط الرسمي(داسيا)يستخدم في الصين	零	壹	貳	參	肆	伍	陆	柒	捌	玖	拾	佰	仟

أدخلت الأرقام العربية لأول مرة في الصين أثناء سلالة مينغ (1368-1644). وفي حقبة سلالة كنج (1644-1912) إستبدل نظام ترميز الأرقام الصينية بالأرقام العربية في الكتابات الرياضية. اليوم الأطفال في الصين يتعلّمون رموز الأرقام الصينية من خلال دروس اللغة الصينيه أما جميع الدراسات الرياضية فتستخدم الأرقام العربية.

من الجدير بالذكر أن نظام ترميز الأرقام الصينية التقليدية هو نفسه المستخدم في اليابان وكوريا. حيث يستخدم في النصوص المكتوبة العمودية في هذه الدول بينما تستخدم الأرقام العربية في النصوص المكتوبة أفقياً وفي المجال الرياضي وهي الأكثر شيوعاً. في بعض الأحيان يستخدم نظام ترميز الأرقام الصيني جنباً إلى جنب مع الأرقام العربية في نفس الصفحة. أيضاً الشعب الصيني يستخدم الأرقام الصينية بنفس الطريقة التي تستخدم فيها الثقافات الغربية الأرقام الرومانيةً أي للأغراض الرسمية ولجمالية الخط من الناحية الفنية.

4 - نظام العد الإغريقي (اليوناني)

لا شك أن للإغريق دوراً بارزاً في تقدم الحضارة المادية ، لكن ينبغي أن نعلم أنهم استفادوا كثيراً من الحضارات التي سبقتهم كالسومرية والآشورية والبابلية والمصرية القديمة والهندية ، كما استفادوا كثيراً من الفينيقيين الذين استعملوا في الألف الأولى قبل الميلاد الحروف العددية ، فتعلم الإغريق من الفينيقيين الكتابة - ولم يكونوا يعرفونها - وأخذوا عنهم حروفهم واستعملوها مدة طويلة في كتابتهم ، وكذلك في الرمز لأرقامهم على قول ، إلى أن تغيّرت لغتهم بمرور الزمن فتغيرت بذلك الحروف.

وقد اعتمد الإغريق والرومان النظام العشري في العد، وهم يكتبون أرقامهم من اليسار إلى اليمين، وثمة تقارب بين الأرقام الإغريقية والرومانية، أنظر الشكل أدناه:

⌐ᴹ	M	⌐ˣ	X	⌐ᴴ	H	⌐Δ	Δ	Γ	I	أشكال الأرقام عند الإغريق
50000	10000	5000	1000	500	100	50	10	5	1	القيمة العددية لها

فيلاحظ أن الفئة الخمسية - سوى الخمسة، وهي (50.500.5000.50000) جمع فيها على التوالي - بين الخمسة والعشرة، والخمسة والمائة، والخمسة والألف، والخمسة والعشرة آلاف .

وقد استعمل الأيونيون – وهم قَبيل من الإغريق – حروفهم للتعبير عن الأرقام، وميزوا بين الحرف والرقم بوضع إشارة أعلى الرقم .

وعَرَف البطالمة – وهم إغريق مصر – الصفر، وصورته عندهم (O). ويبدو أنهم اقتبسوه مع النظام الستيني من البابليين (وقد قال الدكتور ألبرت ديتريش في مقاله – دور العرب في تطوّر العلوم الطبيعية – «وقد اقتبس اليونان من المصريين والبابليين الكثير من علوم الرياضيات والفلك والطب»)، أو أنهم تعلّموه من الهنود، وربما كان من اختراعهم.

إستعمل الإغريق (وكذلك العبريون والعرب قديماً) حروفهم الهجائية في تمثيل الأعداد. وتوضيحاً للنظام الإغريقي نستخدم الحروف α (ألفا)، β (بيتا)، ι (أيوتا)، κ (كبا) حيث تدل على الأعداد: واحد، إثنين...... عشرة، عشرين على الترتيب. وبينما تدل ιβ، على (عشرة وإثنان) أي 12 فإنه لم يكن ممكناً تبادلهما كما هو الشأن في الرموز الحالية. إذ نستطيع الآن تبديل رقمي 12 إلى 21 لدلالة على واحد وعشرين. أما عند الإغريق فإن 21 يدل عليهما الرمز κα وقد ترتب على عدم وصول الإغريق إلى فكرة القيمة المكانية إن استخدموا جميع الحروف الهجائية الأربعة والعشرين بالإضافة إلى ثلاث رموز أخرى في كتابة الأعداد الأساسية الأخرى فهي Γ (جاما) للدلالة على خمسة، H (ايتا) للدلالة على 100، X (خى) للدلالة على 1000، ولكتابة أى عدد كانت تتكرر هذه الأرقام باستخدام طريقة التجميع كما فعل المصريون القدماء، وبمرور الوقت توصل اليونانيون إلى طريقة تسمح لهم باختصار الرموز تسمى (بالطريقة الضربية) في كتابة الأرقام فمثلاً H تعني خمسمائة. ويلاحظ أن هذه الطريقة لا تستعمل إلّا للتعبير عن عدد يساوي حاصل ضرب رقم خمسة. أنظر الجدول أدناه:

كان من نعم الله على الإغريق أن اتصلوا بالأمم القديمة اتصالاً تجارياً، فعرفوا فلسفة هذه الأمم وفنونها وأساطيرها، ولما نشطت الحركة التجارية بينهم وبين المصريين حوالي القرن السابع قبل الميلاد، نهلوا من معارف الكهنة المصريين، وبذلك نقلت الأفكار المصرية عبر البحار إلى بلاد الإغريق.

التسمية	الحرف الصغير	الحرف الكبير
ألفا	α	A
بيتا	β	B
جاما	γ	Γ
دلتا	δ	Δ
إيسيلون	ε	E
زيتا	ζ	Z
إيتا	η	H
ثيتا	θ	Θ
إيوتا	ι	I
كابا	κ	K
لامدا	λ	Λ
ميو	μ	M
نيو	ν	N
إكساي	ξ	Ξ
أوميكرون	o	O
رو	ρ	P
باي	π	Π
سيجما	σ	Σ
تاف	τ	T
أبسيلون	υ	Y
فاي	φ	Φ
خي	χ	X
إيساي	ψ	Ψ
أوميجا	ω	Ω

وقد كانت طريقتهم في كتابة الأعداد تشبه طريقة قدماء المصريين، ثم استخدموا الحروف الأبجدية، ولذلك كان حسابهم معقداً، وفيما يلي شكل الأرقام عند الإغريق:

I	△	H	X	M
1	10	100	1000	10000
⌐	△	H	X	
5	50	500	5000	

شكل الأرقام عند الإغريق وتشبه طريقة المصريين القدماء

5 - نظام العد الروماني

يحتوي نظام العد الروماني على لمحة من فكرة القيمة المكانية – كما سنرى – ويعتقد أن أساس النظام العددي الروماني هو العد بالأصابع يدل على ذلك أن الكلمة اللاتينية للأصبع هي Jigitus وتستخدم الآن كلمة مشتقة منها هي digit التي تستخدم في وصف أي رمز من رموزهم العددية. وقد كتب الرومان الأعداد من واحد إلى أربعة كما يلي:

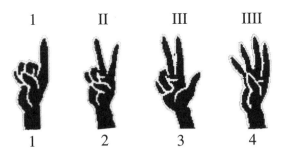

أما رمز خمسة فقد كان علامة على شكل V ولعلها تمثل الفجوة بين الإبهام وبقية الأصابع كما بالشكل أدناه:

وقد نشأت عندهم فكرة القيمة المكانية مرتبطة بهذا الرمز؛ فلكي يتجنبوا التضخم
في كتابة العدد I أربعة مرات هكذا IIII وضعوا I إلى يسار V وطبّقت نفس الفكرة في
رموز أخرى، وأصبح مفهوما أنه إذا كتب الرمز إلى يسار رمز آخر قيمته أكبر فإن
العدد يدل على الفرق بين الرمزين وإذا كتب على يمينه فإن العدد يدل على مجموع
الرمزين ، وقد نشأ هذا التعبير بالأصابع عن الأعداد 6 ، 7 ، 8 كما بالشكل:

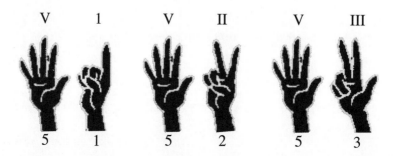

وللتعبير عن العدد 9 كتب I على يسار الرمز الدال على عشرة وهو X ولعله مأخوذ من
وضع اليدين متقاطعتين. وإذن فالعدد 9 يكتب هكذا IX ثم العدد 10 يكتب X ثم العدد
11 ويدل عليه الرمز XI حيث يوضع الرمز المعبر عن العدد واحد على يمين رمز العشرة
ليدل ذلك على مجموع الرقمين وهكذا، وبذلك فإن الأرقام الرومانية الأولى هي:

الأرقام الرومانية الأولى	IX	VIII	VII	VI	V	IV	III	II	I
ما يقابلها من الأرقام المعاصرة	9	8	7	6	5	4	3	2	1
الأرقام الرومانية الأولى		XIV	XIII	XII	XI	X			
ما يقابلها من الأرقام المعاصرة		14	13	12	11	10			

وهكذا إلى عشرين XX ثم ثلاثين XXX

ولتجنب تكرار رمز أربع مرات للدلالة على 40 هكذا XXXX وضع رمز L للدلالة على العدد خمسين ويعتقد أنه النصف الأسفل من حرف C الدال على مائة وهو الحرف الأول من كلمة Centum (أي مائة)، وعلى ذلك فإن العدد 40 يكتب هكذا XL بينما تدل LX على العدد ستين، كذلك فإن XC تدل على 90 بينما CX تدل على مائة وعشرة (110) ثم استخدم حرف M للدلالة على العدد ألف (1000) ربما لأن M هو الحرف الأول من كلمة Mille اللاتينية بمعنى ألف (1000) وقبل ذلك كان يتم التعبير عن العدد 1000 بالحرف Φ (فاي) اليوناني ثم كتب بصورة بسيطة هكذا (l) وهذا تحور إلى M للدلالة على 1000 أما العدد 500 فقد كان يتم التعبير عنه بالرمز ⊃| وهو كما ترى الجزء الأيمن من حرف (l) فاي في صورته البسيطة ثم تحور الرمز ⊃| الدال على خمسمائة إلى حرف D. والجدول التالي يبين باختصار الرموز الأساسية لنظام العد الروماني:

M	D	C	L	X	V	I
1000	500	100	50	10	5	1

وعلى ذلك فإن العدد MXDVIII يدل على 1408، والعدد MMCCCXXLV يدل على 2335، والعام 1999 يدل عليه العدد MCMXCIX وهكذا...

المصدر: www.alargam.com

6 – الأرقام الهندية

هناك مجموعة أرقام هندية قديمة تسمى بالخاروشتية الشعبية: وهذه بدأت تتخلق في القرن الثالث قبل الميلاد، ثم اتخذت في مدى قرنين أشكالاً بينية، ولكنها لا تنطوي على فكرة منازلية، وقد وجد (سمث) و(كاربنسكي) شبها بين هذه الأشكال وبين الحروف النبطية، ولكنهما استبعدا أن تكون الأشكال الخاروشتية هي أصول الأرقام الهندية التي وصلت إلى العرب والأوروبيين، وإليك بعض تلك الأشكال:

أما المجموعة الأخرى التي أشار إليها (سمث) و(كاربنسكي): فهي المجموعة البراهمية، وقد اعتبراها الأصل الذي نجمت عنه الحروف الديوانجارية، (قال الدكتور سعيدان في بحثه: علم الحساب عند العرب ص. 180 حاكياً عن (سمث) و(كاربنسكي): «إن صور الأرقام يبدو أنها انحدرت من صور حروف ديوانجارية هي أصول الحروف السنسكريتية التي تكتب بها اللغة البراهمية». وذكر الدكتور بخاري في كتابه الأرقام العربية ص. 34 أن الأبجدية البراهمية انتشر استخدامها بشكل واسع في جميع أنحاء الهند في حدود القرن الثالث قبل الميلاد – في كتاب الدكتور بخاري : بعد الميلاد، ولعل الصواب ما ذكرته، ويُنظرالعد والترقيم عند العرب 80/4 عندما وحد أسوكا نواحي الهند). وهي أمهات الأرقام السنسكريتية الحاضرة. ولكن (سمث) و(كاربنسكي) لم يستطيعا أن يجزما بأنها أمهات الأرقام العربية».

وتابع الدكتور سعيدان حديثه عن رأي الباحثين الغربيين في تلك المراحل فقال: «أما (درنجر) فكان همه أن يدرس تاريخ الأبجديات وتطورها: أما عن الأبجدية الخاروشتية فيؤكد أن هذه كانت أبجدية العامة، يستعملونها في حياتهم اليومية، ولذا فلا ننتظر أن نجدها في النقوش والكتابات الدينية، وهو يؤكد أنها كانت تتجه من اليمين إلى الشمال حتى عصر متأخر عكس فيه اتجاهها، وأنها كانت تستعمل في شرقي أفغانستان وجنوب البنجاب. ويعتقد (درنجر) أنها وليدة الحروف الآرامية السامية... أما عن الأبجدية البراهمية فيرجح (درنجر) أنها هي أيضا وليدة الأبجدية الآرامية».

وقد ذكر الدكتور بخاري نماذج للأرقام البراهمية القديمة على النحو التالي :

وذكر بعدها أشكال الأرقام البراهمية المتطورة، التي عمل بها منذ القرن الثاني بعد الميلاد، وهي على النحو التالي :

ثم تعرّض لإظهار شكل الأرقام النجارية – نسبة إلى منطقة نجاري – حسب تطورها، ذاكراً أن القديم منها يشبه الأرقام البراهمية، وقد أوردها على النحو التالي:

وذكر الدكتور عبد الستار محمد فيض شكلين للأرقام الهندية، وصورتهما هكذا:

وأما أشكال الأرقام الهندية كما تحكيها أقدم الكتب العربية - التي وصلت إلينا -
في الحساب الهندي (أول كتاب عربي في الحساب هو لمحمد بن موسى الخوارزمي،
وهو مفقود، لكن مجموعة كبيرة من المخطوطات اللاتينية نقلت عنه واقتبست منه،
بيد أن الأرقام والعمليات الحسابية المنسوبة للخوارزمي ضمن هذه الرسائل
اللاتينية تختلف اختلافا كليا عما انتشر عند العرب - في المشرق والمغرب - من
أرقام وطريقة حساب. قصة الأرقام والترقيم ص. 68-69، علم الحساب عند
العرب، ص.181-182)، فأعرضها من خلال الكتب التالية:

ففي كتاب الفصول في الحساب الهندي لأبي الحسن أحمد بن إبراهيم الإقليدسي
- وهو أول ما وصل إلينا منها، وقد وضعه مؤلفه في دمشق سنة (341 ه): «الباب
الأول: في معرفة الأحرف التسعة والمراتب: إن أول ما ينبغي أن يعلم من ذلك لمن
ابتدأ بهذا العلم: معرفة الأحرف التسعة، وهي هذه:

$$ ٩ ٨ ٧ ٦ ٥ ٤ ٣ ٢ ١ $$

المصدر : www.alargam.com

استخدام الأرقام عند العرب المسلمين

يرجع الفضل الأكبر لتعاليم الإسلام في اهتمام المسلمين بالرياضيات وكافة العلوم
المختلفة، وكانت هذه التعاليم ولا تزال تحض على العلم وطلبه «فالعلم فريضة على
كل مسلم ومسلمة»، «واطلبوا العلم ولو بالصين»، كما توجّه الأنظار إلى السماوات

وما فيها، وإلى الأرض وما عليها وتتطلب الأحوال الشخصية وما فيها من مواريث، والمعاملات التجارية وما فيها من عقود إلى أجل مسمى، معرفة التقاويم، والأصول الحسابية والهندسية كما تتطلب العبادات معرفة مواقيت الصلاة وتعيين سمة القبلة، ومعرفة هلال رمضان ووقت الحج... الخ، مما يقتضي تتبع حركة الشمس، القمر، كل هذا دعا إلى البحث وراء العلوم وخصوصاً علم الفلك الذي يستلزم معرفة الرياضيات المختلفة من حساب المثلثات، وهندسة وجبر، وكل ما يمتّ بصلة إلى علوم الطبيعة وما وراءها.

كيف اتصل العرب بالحضارات الأخرى ؟

إتصل العرب بالإغريق عن طريق السريانيين في آسيا الصغرى، وبواسطتهم اتصلوا بمسيحيي الإغريق، وعن طريق الرحلات والأسفار، وعن طريق إستدعاء الخلفاء لعلماء الإغريق، ونقلهم إلى اللغة العربية العلوم الإغريقية، كما اتصل العرب بالفرس والهنود، واتصلوا بهم اتصالاً وثيقاً، وبهذا تعدّدت ثقافات العرب وحضاراتهم وفي أيام عثمان بن عفان، كان اتصال العرب بالهنود، وفي أثناء فتح الحجاج الثقفي للسند، 710 م، وفي أثناء فتح أبي جعفر المنصور لكابل وكشمير سنة 760 م.

ويرى الباحثون، أن فضل العرب على الإنسانية كبير وذلك لما يلي:

1 - كانوا حفظة أمناء للكنوز العلمية الإغريقية، وأبقوها سليمة مزدهرة، وأنقذوها من الرومان.

2 - كانوا وسيلة لإظهار الكنوز العلمية الهندية التي ازدهرت في المشرق، في الوقت الذي ازدهرت فيه العلوم الإغريقية في المغرب.

3 - وصلوا بين العلوم الإغريقية والعلوم الهندية ومزجوا بينها، وسلموها سليمة نقية إلى الغربيين حينما هبوا من سباتهم، وخلعوا عن أكتافهم رداء الخمول، ونزحوا إلى الأندلس حيث جامعات اشبيلية وقرطبة وغرناطة، وإلى غير الأندلس، باحثين وراء هذه العلوم وتعلموا اللغة العربية، ونقلوا ما أخذوه عن العرب إلى اللغة اللاتينية.

4 – أضافوا إلى العلوم التي أخذوها، فتوحات علمية زاهرة، وكشوفات قيمة جديدة نسبت لغيرهم، وظن أنها كشفت بعدهم.

ما هي قصة الأرقام العربية؟

لا شك في أن العرب والمسلمين شأنهم شأن أصحاب الحضارات الأخرى يتأثرون بغيرهم ويؤثرون فيهم، ولكن البعض يقع في الخطأ عندما يعتبر أن الأرقام العربية أرقاما هندية، أو أن الصفر ليس عربيا، أو أن الأصح أن تكتب الأرقام العربية هكذا:
٠٩٨٧٦٥٤٣٢١

وهذا يرجع إلى أن الأمور العلمية أصبح يختلط فيها الحابل في النابل وأصبحت غير واضحة لكثير من الناس. ولكن القصة تبدأ عندما اطلع العرب على الأنظمة المختلفة للترقيم عند الشعوب التي أخضعوها والتي كانت تربط بينهم وبينها أواصر الصداقة. استحسنوا النظام الهندي، وكان عند هؤلاء، أشكالا متعددة، فأخذ العرب وانتقوا منها ما رأوه مناسباً واكتفوا بطريقتين مختلفتين لكتابة الأرقام:

1 – الطريقة المشرقية، واستعملها عرب بغداد، وتطورت قليلا حتى أصبحت الأرقام التي نستعملها الآن في مصر والعراق وسوريا ولبنان وفلسطين وبلاد العرب وهي: ٠٩٨٧٦٥٤٣٢١

2 – الطريقة المغاربية واستعملها عرب الأندلس، وتطورت قليلا حتى أصبحت الأرقام التي تستعمل الآن في بلاد المغرب وهي: 0987654321

وقد أخذ الغربيون الطريقة المغاربية عن طريق الأندلس حيث عكسو تسلسلها من اليمين الى اليسار لتتماشى مع طريقة كتابتهم. ولا يزال دول المغرب العربي الآن يستعملون طريقة أجدادهم في كتابة الأرقام، فلا يظن ظان بأنهم يكتبون الأرقام الإفرنجية، وإنما الفرنجة هم الذين يكتبون الأرقام عن الطريقة المغاربية، ولا يزال الغرب يطلق على هذه الأرقام اسم الأرقام العربية.

الفصل الثاني

ما هي قصة الصفر لدى علماء المسلمين؟

ينكر كثير من الباحثين أن يكون «الصفر» هنديا، ويصر البعض الآخر على أنه عربياً.

والواقع أن الصفر وغيره من الأرقام ليس في شكله بقدر ما هو في قيمته الوضعية، ويمكن بواسطتها أن نعبر عن أكبر عدد وأصغر عدد فيكفي أن نزيد في الأصفار عن يمين مقام الكسر ليصغر.

ويرى بعض الباحثين أن شكل الصفر عند الهنود يكتب دائرة فيها نقطة هكذا ⊙ وكان ذلك في المدة الأخيرة، أي خانة خالية، وقد أخذ عرب المشرق النقطة وتركوا الدائرة، وأخذ العرب المغارب الدائرة وتركوا النقطة.

ويرى البعض الآخر أن الحُساب المسلمين كانوا يعرفون الصورة الإغريقية للصفر أي دائرة فوقها خط ويصل النساخ أحيانا بين الدائرة والخط الذي فوقها.

وعلى ذلك تصبح الصورة الكاملة للصفر لدى الإغريق هي ذاتها الصورة الهندية، وخاصة إذا علمنا التقليد الهندي لكتابة الأرقام كان يقتضي أن يوضع خط فوق الرقم وعلى الرغم من هذا، وكما قلت في بداية الكلام عن الصفر أن العرب حددوا قيمة الصفر واستخدامه، أما موضوع شكله، فهو نقل حضاري وقبل النقل فهو اختيار من متعدد، وتطويعه بالشكل الأخير ليصبح للعرب أرقام سواء بالطريقة المشرقية أو بالطريقة المغاربية.

بحث يكشف سر الأرقام العربية

توصّلنا بموقع الأرقام من الأستاذ عبد الحي الدكالي من المغرب بحث عددي، يكشف سر الأرقام العربية نعرضه فيما يلي:

في هذا الجدول يأخذ الحرف الأبجدي قيمة الرقم الذي يقابله.

جدول حساب الجُمَّل

الرقم المقابل	الحرف الأبجدي	الرقم المقابل	الحرف الأبجدي
20	ك	1	أ
30	ل	2	ب
40	م	3	ج
50	ن	4	د
60	س	5	ه
70	ع	6	و
80	ف	7	ز
90	ص	8	ح
100	ق	9	ط
200	ر	10	ي
400	ت	300	ش
600	خ	500	ث
800	ض	700	ذ
1000	غ	900	ظ

إستخدم العرب منذ الجاهلية إلى صدر العصر العباسي حساب الجمل (الموسوعة العربية العالمية). وأكثر ما استخدم حساب الجمل لتدوين تاريخ الأحداث.

إذا جمعنا قيم حروف وهدَفي حساب 6+5+4+10+8+80+60+1+2 نجد 176.

176 هجرية تأتي في الفترة التي حكم فيها إدريس الأول المغرب، من 172 إلى 177 هجرية، وفي الفترة التي حكم فيها هارون الرشيد المشرق، من 170 إلى 193 هجرية.

سبعة من قيم حروف وهدَفي حساب آحاد في جدول حساب الجمل.

في 176 هجرية كان يسود الخط الكوفي. وهذه التسمية تطلق على كل الخطوط التي تميل إلى التربيع والهندسة.

إذن الشكل الذي هو في الأسفل خط كوفي ويقرأ: وهدَفي حسـاب.

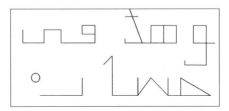

وبتفكيكنا هذه الجملة إلى حروف نحصل على:

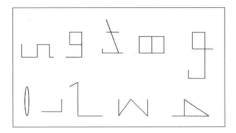

أي :

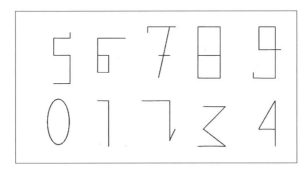

وهكذا بعد أن بقي الواو والسكون كما هو، ودورنا الهاء والفاء والياء والحاء والسين والألف والباء، وقلبنا الدال، حصلنا على الأرقام العربية.

0 9 8 7 6 5 4 3 2 1

كل الأرقام هي على شكلها الحالي إلا الرقم 2. إن قلبناه حصلنا على حرف الحاء.

الفصل الثالث

العولمة والأرقام

1 - في الإقتصاد: لقد أصبح الإقتصاد المحلي والدولي يعتمد على الأرقام أن 50٪ من اللغة الإقتصادية ما بين الأمم تعتمد على الأرقام وما تبقى هي عبارة عن شروحات لهذه الأرقام وهي شروحات ومصطلحات موحدة للمعاني المتعارف عليها.

2 - في الرياضيات: إن الرياضيات تعتمد على ما لا يقل عن 70 ٪ على الأرقام وإن الحروف التي تستعمل في الرياضيات للترميز تمثل 15٪، بالإضافة الى فواصل التعريف (+ ، - ، = ، ٪... الخ).

3 - الإلكترونيات وعلوم الاتصالات هي أيضاً تعتمد على الأرقام اعتماداً كلياً.

4 - الكيمياء والعلوم الأخرى مثل إحصائيات النفوس وغيرها تعتمد على الأرقام.

5 - معظم دول العالم باستثناء دول المشرق العربي اليوم تستعمل الأرقام العربية والتي سميت في كتابنا هذا أرقامنا العربية حيث إنها أصبحت لغة الأرقام المشتركة مابين الأمم المستعملة لها.

6 - إن الصفر (0) الذي تمت به ديناميكية الأرقام هو في الواقع في الأرقام المشرقية سبباً وعلة في كثير من الأخطاء حيث اختلطت الأصفار المشرقية مع النتوءات والنقاط الأخرى في الكتابة أو عدم ظهوره بوضوح في الكتابة أو الطباعة فأي خلل بعد هذا الخلل في أرقامنا المشرقية.

7 - إن معظم الكتابات الحضارية لا بدّ من أن تعتمد على استعمال الأرقام بنسب مختلفة والمكان الوحيد الذي لا يستعمل الأرقام بكثرة هي الكتب والمقالات الأدبية والتاريخية وغيرها من القصص.

8 – إن أمتنا إذا أرادت أن تدخل العولمة وتعرف العالم على تراثها وحضاراتها لا بدّ من تغيير الأرقام من المشرقية إلى أرقامنا العربية وبذلك تُحل 50٪ من لغة التفاهم ما بين الأمم وتسهل مهمة الباحثين والقارئين وستتضاعف الفائدة بنسبة 50 ٪ في حقول الإبداع الفني والإنتاجي .

أخيراً، إن كل ما هو سلبي في أرقامنا المشرقية من شكل وعزلة وعن سير حضارة الأرقام العالمية سيكون إيجابياً في حالة التغيير إلى أرقامنا العربية.

الفصل الرابع

القادة الذين خلقوا التغيير
وطوروا الحضارات عبر العصور

القادة الذين خلقوا التغيير وطوروا الحضارات عبر العصور

إنّ الأمم لا تنهض من كبوتها أو سباتها إلاّ بثورات علميّة أو ثقافيّة أو تكنولوجيّة يسجلها أبناؤها وينشرها أو يحقّقها أو ينفّذها قادتها. لنستعرض بعض ما جاء عبر العصور وفي عصرنا هذا:

1 - لو تمعّنا النظر في فقرة تاريخ تطّور الأرقام في هذا الكتاب لوجدنا عبر العصور أن هناك رجال فكر وإبداع وقادة نفّذوا إبداعات الأفراد وخلقوا الثورات التغييرية في حضاراتهم.

2 - وهذا البحث الوارد في هذا الكتاب يروي بعض جوانب تطّور الأرقام وفضلها على العلوم التكنولوجية الحديثة، ولولا ما وصلت إليه الأرقام من مضمون وشكل وما استقرّت عليه البشرية، ما كان لنا اليوم كل هذا الشرف حين يشار إلى الأرقام العربية. وكانت الأرقام خير ذخيرة وخير كنوز إسلامية تركها المسلمون بعدما هزموا من أوروبا، ألم يحن الوقت لاسترجاعها وللإستفادة منها بعدما أصبحت الأرقام العربية المفاتيح السحرية للعلوم التكنولوجية الحديثة بشكلها السائد استعماله عالمياً.

3 - كما تقول الآية الكريمة (عَلَّمَ الإِنسَانَ مَا لَمْ يَعْلَمْ – سورة العلق/5) أما إرادة العمل هي من عندنا والتي أتت الآيات الكريمة كلها تحث على العمل الصالح (وأما ما ينفع الناس فيمكث في الأرض– سورة الرعد/17)

4 - لقد شاهدت فيلما عن حياة هتلر عرض في ألمانيا بعد الحرب في أواخر الخمسينيات وقد عرض في حينه في كل مدينة في أكثر من ثلاثة دور سينما وكان الإقبال عليه شديداً خاصة من قبل الشباب، كانت قصة حياة هتلر منذ ظهوره على مسرح السياسة وكانت معظم الصور هي أفلام وقائعية أخذت خلال حياته وأخرى مصوّرة لغرض تسلسل قصة الفيلم وكان معظم فقرات الفيلم منصبّاً على الثورات التكنولوجية والعمرانية التي تحقّقت في عهده وكذلك الحرب الذي خاضها والتي أتت على كل شيء إلاّ على العقول التي بقت لتنير ألمانيا وتضعها ثانية في مقدمة الأمم وكانت آخر كلمة ألقيت في الفيلم عن هتلر هي أنه لو لم يدخل هتلر السياسة لكان أعظم وأشمل مهندس أخرجته البشرية.

ولا غرابة في ذلك حيث سبقه بسمارك في توحيده ألمانيا وسبقه غوتيه في وضع القواعد وتوحيد اللغة الألمانية.

واليوم وأنا في الحيرة التي لازمتني منذ عدة أشهر بأن أبدأ بكتابة كتابي هذا الذي تراودني فكرته منذ بضعة سنوات، دار في نشرات الأخبار خبر حول إصدار مرسوم قبل أكثر من سنة في ألمانيا يضع قواعد جديدة مبسطة لإملاء أكثر من مائتين كلمة ألمانية متداولة أي تغيير حروفها لتسهل على التعلّم والذاكرة وغيرها، و لم يغفل في عصرنا هذا علماء ألمانيا حتى من قواعد لغتهم التي هي من المفروض أن تكون رمزاً لأمجادهم واعتزازهم، وكان قادتها قمة في التقدير والتقييم والقدرة على الأخذ بها والانطلاق نحو التغيير وكان الخبر هو عن المعارضين لتطبيق القواعد الجديدة من قبل بعض دور النشر التي سوف تتضرّر بسبب عدم بيع مطبوعاتها المدرسية وغيرها ممن لهم وجهة نظر مختلفة في حقول التعليم، ندرج هنا ما ورد في الجريدة:

قواعد الهجاء الجديدة في اللغة الألمانية

اللغة التي لا تجد من يتحدثها أو يكتب بها مآلها الزوال

وما أن بدأ تطبيق قواعد هجاء جديدة ترمي إلى تسهيل استعمال اللغة الألمانية حتى جوبهت بنقد قاس في كل من ألمانيا والنمسا وسويسرا حيث وصفها الناطقون بالألمانية بأنها «مربكة» و«تافهة».

وذكرت وكالة الأنباء الألمانية أن هذا التغيير يمس 212 قاعدة هجاء و 52 قاعدة حول مكان الفاصلة مما خفض مجموع قواعد الهجاء إلى 112 وقواعد الفاصلة إلى تسعة فقط في لغة تكبّلها المئات من القواعد الأخرى المعقدة والغريبة التركيب.

ويقول المدافعون عن النظام الجديد إنه سيجعل التعليم أسهل ويساعد على التوثيق في المكاتب والإدارات الحكومية.

وسيسمح بإستخدام القواعد القديمة والجديدة معاً خلال فترة انتقالية تستمر حتى عام 2005 يمكن خلالها للرافضين للتغيير وهم على الأرجح أغلبية ساحقة من

القادة الذين خلقوا التغيير وطوروا الحضارات عبر العصور

الأشخاص الأكبر سناً – الإستمرار في استخدام ما يوصف بطريقة مهذبة بأنه «الكتابة التقليدية».

ووجهت جابريبل بيهلر – التي ترأست اجتماعاً في فيينا لوزراء الثقافة للدول المتحدثة بالألمانية في عام 1996 تم خلاله الموافقة على القواعد الجديدة – نداء إلى وسائل الإعلام والكتاب بأن يتعاونوا في زرع وتنمية القواعد الجديدة.

ولكن معارضي التغيير لم يدخروا وسعاً في إدانة القواعد الجديدة التي قالوا عنها إنها غير منطقية وتعوزها السلاسة إلى جانب أنها في رأيهم تحرم اللغة الألمانية من تراثها الخصب.

ودعت جابريبل روتا المتحدثة باسم المعارضين إلى منع القواعد الجديدة من الصرف؟ وتجاهلها تماما في الأشهر القادمة على أساس أن «اللغة التي لا تجد من يتحدّثها أو يكتب بها مآلها الزوال».

وقد تمّ صرف الملايين من الماركات على كتب دراسية جديدة مبنية على القواعد المعدلة، كما أن المحكمة الدستورية العليا في ألمانيا رفضت مؤخراً التماساً بوقف القواعد الجديدة بزعم أنها تنتهك الحريات الأساسية.

وكان الإلتماس الذي نظرت فيه المحكمة مقدّماً من زوجين من مدينة لوبيك الشمالية يدفع بأن الإصلاحات اللغوية المفروضة تعتبر تدخلاً في حقوقها الشرعية في توجيه تعليم طفليهما اللذين يبلغان من العمر تسع سنوات.

أما في ولاية شلزويج هو لشتين في أقصى الشمال فتمّ إجراء إستفتاء حول ما إذا كان سيتم بالفعل العمل بالقواعد الجديدة في الولاية وذلك يوم السابع والعشرين من سبتمبر، نفس اليوم المحدد للانتخابات العامة في ألمانيا.

ويذكر أن الشعور المناهض للإصلاحات في تلك الولاية على أشدّه بين الدارسين والخبراء والآباء الذين يطالبون حكوماتهم المحلية بأن تشذّ عن القاعدة وتجعل من شلزويج هو لشتين الولاية الوحيدة التي تستمر في العمل بالقواعد «الأصيلة» للغة الألمانية.

ويرتكز الدافع الأساسي للإصلاحات على أن اللغة الألمانية في صورتها الحالية مبنية على المئات من القواعد التي لا تتبع قواعد منطقية عامة محددة مما يجعل حفظها عن ظهر قلب أمرا لا مناص منه بالنسبة للأطفال الألمان ولكل من يريد تعلم الألمانية من غير الألمان.

لقد أحدث انهيار جدار برلين هزّة كبرى في العالم وسرعان ما أعلنت الوحدة بين شطري ألمانيا بغض النظر عن كل ما كلف الإقتصاد الشطر الغربي والمعاناة الإقتصادية التي عاناها شعبها، بغض النظر عن الاختلافات التي ترسّبت ما بين قدرات وأخلاقيات ونظم كل شطر من شطري ألمانيا، لقد وظّفت الحكومة الإتحادية طاقاتها الإقتصادية لتحقيق الوحدة.

لم تكتفٍ وتختصر ألمانيا على القيام في الثورات التغييرية في علومها واقتصادها على ألمانيا بل وضعت اقتصادها و(ماركها) القوي تحت تصرف توحيد الدول الأوربية وأهم إنجازات الوحدة الأوربية هو «اليورو»، لا يخفى على إثنين بأن المارك الألماني واقتصاد ألمانيا هو القلب النابض في تأسيس وتحقيق «اليورو»، ناهيك عن الكلف الإقتصادية، أي علوم وأي تكنولوجيا وأي تنظيم وتعريف وتطبيع يتطلب «اليورو» ليحل محل خمس وعشرين عملة مختلفة بكل معاني الإختلاف شكلاً ومضموناً وقيمة وكيفاً سهل هذا التغيير لشعوب منطقة (اليورو) لكي تأخذ به وتعيش حاضرها ومستقبلها، ألم يعتبر اليورو ثورة حضارية اقتصادية توحيدية تنقل رعايا هذه الأقطار من عالم إلى عالم آخر، نعم إنهم قادة اختارتهم شعوبهم وكانوا أهلاً للاختيار.

5 - ولو أنني لا أقرّ ما قام به أتاتورك عند توليه الحكم بعد انهيار الدولة العثمانية في حل الحروف اللاتينية محل الحروف العربية في لغتهم التركية مما أفقد الشعب التركي هويته وفقدان الأجيال التركية لماضيها وحضاراتها وعلومها وما كانت تتميّز به، أقول بالرغم من عدم إقراري لا بد لي أن أنوّه بالخطوة الجريئة التي أقدم عليها في تبديله الحروف العربية باللاتينية كوسيلة لإنهاض الشعب التركي من ترهّله وسباته نتيجة لتقادم الزمان على حكم خلفاء الدولة العثمانية.

6 - بالرغم مما عرف عن الشعب البريطاني وسياساته المتحفظة وعدم حماسه للتغيير والبرود الذي يتميّز به، كمثال على ذلك هو عطلهم الرسمية حيث كلما جاءت خلال أيام الأسبوع أجّلت إلى يوم الاثنين وتسمى Bank Holiday لا يعرف عامة الناس ما هي مناسبة هذه العطلة باستثناء أعياد Christmas ورأس السنة فهي تعطّل في مواعيدها، أقول بالرغم من ذلك فقد غيّرت الكثير من القواعد وأسس مقاييسها وأوزانها وقد تمّ تغيير العملة من (شلن Shilling) و(كيني Guinea) عام 1971 المعتمدة على أساس اثنا عشر إلى العملة العشرية أي ذات الأجزاء العشرية والمئوية وكذلك تمّ تغيير مقاييس الطول من Foot وYard وMiles إلى المقاييس المترية. وكذلك الأوزان من Ounce وPound إلى الغرام والكيلو أي المقاييس العشرية، بالرغم من أن التغييرات هذه لم تكن سريعة إلّا أن التغيير يسير بشكل هادئ، إن الفرق بين طريقة التغيير الألمانية وطريقة التغيير البريطانية هو أن الأولى تتسم بالثورية والسرعة في التنفيذ والثانية تتسم بالهدوء والتأنّي والمهم عند الطرفين هو الوصول إلى الهدف.

الفصل الخامس

تطور أرقامنا العربية مع عصر الحاسوب (الكومبيوتر)

تطور أرقامنا العربية مع عصر الحاسوب (الكومبيوتر)

في وقت يستعمل المغرب العربي، مثل المملكة المغربية وتونس والجزائر الأرقام العربية العالمية ويعود لهم الفضل في إدخالها إلى أوروبا مع دخول الإسلام إلى بلاد الأندلس، لم ينقل لنا التاريخ بأن الدول المغاربية استعملت الأرقام المشرقية.

نتيجة لذلك أصبح هناك رقمان مختلفا الشكل في كتاباتنا العربية وحتى شمل ترقيم الآيات القرآنية الكريمة هناك الرقم العربي العالمي للدول المغاربية والرقم المشرقي للبلاد التي تستعمل الرقم المشرقي.

عندما بدأ مؤسّسو مؤسّسة الديوان لإعداد البرامج الكومبيوترية باللغة العربية كانوا ثلاثة من الشباب العراقيين النابغين وبطبيعة الحال كانت برامجهم العربية تعتمد على الأرقام المشرقية وبعد عدة سنوات تطورت هذه البرامج وتزامنت مع دخول شركات ومؤسّسات أخرى في إعداد البرامج بالتعاون والدعم مع المؤسسات الكبرى مثل Microsoft و Apple وغيرهم.

بدأت البرامج تأخذ أبعاداً مختلفة لتلبية متطلبات الأمم ولغاتها أما بقدر ما يتعلق الأمر بأرقامنا العربية فقد تم عمل برنامجين عربيين مختلفين أحدهما يحوي الأرقام المشرقية والآخر يحوي الأرقام العربية العالمية، وأخيراً تمكن المبرمجون من وضع الرقمين محل الإستعمال عبر الإنتقال من الرقم المشرقي إلى أرقامنا العربية أو بالعكس بسهولة فائقة أي بالنقر على عدة أزرار ويأتي الشكل المطلوب للرقم كما هو الحال في اختيار أنواع وأشكال الحروف الأبجدية والتي تتغير أشكالها وأحجامها حسب الطلب.

1 - ظهور بوادر التغيير في أرقامنا العربية

أ - لقد أخذت بعض التلفزيونات العربية في استعمال أرقامنا العربية بدلاً من الأرقام المشرقية على شاشاتها، إلاّ أن ذلك لم يتم على ما أعتقد على أسس استراتيجية أو منهجية منظّمة فتارة تخرج البيانات بالأرقام المشرقية وتارة أخرى بأرقامنا العربية وعلى نفس الشاشة، أي أن رياح التغيير في الأرقام أخذت تهب ولكن بشكل عشوائي.

الفصل الخامس

ب - الصحافة

لا تزال الصحافة المحلية العربية تتبع نظام الأرقام التي يعتمد عليها بلدها.

أما الصحافة العربية الدولية مثل جريدة الشرق الأوسط والحياة والقدس وغيرها التي تصدر خارج البلاد العربية أخذت تعتمد على أرقامنا العربية بدلا من الأرقام المشرقية التي تتبعها بلدانها.

ج - الكتب والمجلات

على ما أعتقد لم يتم التحرك والتحسس في تغيير نوعية الأرقام فيها بمثل ما أخذت بوادر التغيير في وسائط الإعلام ربما هناك بعض الإستثناءات في بعض الكتب وأخص منها كتابي (العبادات المالية في الإسلام) وكتاب (الجهاد الإنساني في الإسلام).

د - لم نسمع أو نقرأ أي بوادر تغيير في المناهج الدراسية في أي قطر من الأقطار التي أرقامها المشرقية فإن التعليم لا زال يعتمد على الرقمين أي الرقم المشرقي للغة العربية وأرقامنا العربية للغات اللاتينية.

توصيات الدراسة

بعدما تأكد لنا أن العرب كان لهم الفضل الأكبر في نقل نتائج حضارات من سبقهم إلى الإنسانية، وأن اهتمام العرب أنفسهم بما لدى الإغريق والهنود قاد إلى استخدام النظام الحسابي المطور في شكله العربي الأخير وعلى ذلك فأنني أرى وأوصي بالتوصيات التالية:

1 - ينبغي أن لا نتمسك بالشكليات ونقول أيهما أصح الطريقة المشرقية وهي:

٠٩٨٧٦٥٤٣٢١ أم الطريقة المغاربية وهي: 0987654321

ولكن يجب أن نقرّر أن كلا الطريقتين عربيتان أما ما شاع في العالم فهو أرقامنا العربية وأطلق عليها بالأرقام العربية.

تطور أرقامنا العربية مع عصر الحاسوب (الكومبيوتر)

2 - ينبغي أن نرجع في دراستنا وننبه إلى الإهتمام بفضل العرب وعلماء المسلمين في قيامهم بالدور الحضاري ونشير إلى البيروني والخوارزمي واليعقوبي والأقليدس فالبيروني في كتبه عن الهند يذكر بأمانة أنه لقي الهنود ووجدهم يستعملون مجموعات شتى من الأرقام وأن ما أخذه العرب هو أحسن ما عند الهنود، والبيروني عاش في الفترة 973 - 1048 م وأول كاتب عربي كتب في الحساب الهندي هو أبو جعفر محمد بن موسى الخوارزمي الذي عاش في عصر المأمون، وكتاب الخوارزمي عمل في مكتبة الخليفة المأمون في الفترة من 813-833 م وأقدم وصف عربي نعرفه للأرقام الهندية نجده في كتاب اليعقوبي (التاريخ) الذي إنتهى فيه إلى أحداث الأقليدس، وقد كتبه في دمشق سنة 341 هـ 952/953 م).

3 - أن ثلثي عدد الأرقام في السلسلتين الهندية (المشرقية) وأرقامنا العربية يكاد يكون شكلها واحداً في السلسلتين، ولاسيما إذا ما عرف أن التطور اقتصر في بعضها على انحراف زاوية سمة أو على انحناء مخالف، أو على استطالة في بعض أجزائها أو اختصار كما في الأرقام 0987654321.

4 - ينبغي التأكيد على أن كلا الشكلين المغربي والمشرقي عربي بعد تعديلات على الشكل الهندي، وهذا يعتبر من ابتكار الحضارة العربية، هذا من ناحية، ومن ناحية أخرى علينا أن نؤكد على أن العبرة كذلك والفضل الأكبر للعرب لاستخدامهم الأرقام في العمليات الحسابية المختلفة وجعل قيمة للصفر حتى رغم وجوده عند الإغريق والهنود.

وأخيرا آن الأوان لعودة أرقامنا العربية إلى أحضان الأمة

متطلبات الإعداد لاستقبال أرقامنا العربية المهاجرة إلى العالم

1 - قيام الجامعة العربية بإعداد دراسة أوليّة ولائحة توضيحيّة وإعدادها على شكل مشروع تقدّمه إلى الحكومات العربية لإقراره لبدء تفاصيل إعتماد أرقامنا العربية لتحل محل الأرقام المشرقية التي تستعمل حالياً في معظم الدول العربية، على أن يتمّ التغيير خلال مدة زمنية لا تتجاوز الثلاث سنوات أو على أقصى حد الخمس سنوات.

الفصل الخامس

2 - تكوين لجان علمية من قبَل وزارات التعليم ووزارات التخطيط ووزارات الإعلام والثقافة كلاً على حدة، لتضع توصياتها، وبعدها يجتمع ممثلي هذه اللجان في اجتماع موسع لإقرار الصيغة النهائية لوسائل وطرق التغيير ومواعيد تنفيذها.

3 - إن تعذّر تحقيق ذلك عن طريق الجامعة العربية، فلتقم كل دولة مشرقيّة باعتماد أرقامنا العربية وذلك عن طريق تقرير الأرقام في المناهج الدراسيّة إلى أرقامنا العربية وفرضها على دور الإعلام والنشر وغيرها.

4 - لنجعل من هذا التغيير في الأرقام ثورة علمية ثقافية تتفجّر من خلالها طاقات أمتنا العلمية والإبداعية، خاصة في علوم الحاسوب (الكومبيوتر) والبرمجة والتنظيم من خلال فسح المجال والإعتماد على الأفراد والقطاع الخاص في أن يأخذ دوره في العمل والمشاركة في عملية التغيير، وبذلك تتفتّح آفاق العمل والرزق أمام آلاف المفكرين والمبدعين من أمتنا، وبذلك ننقذ عملية التغيير الكبرى في الأرقام من التمرجح مابين شكلين من الأرقام.

«وقل إعملو فسيرى اللّه عملكم ورسوله والمؤمنون – سورة التوبة 105». واللّه ولي التوفيق.

المراجع والهوامش

Joy, RR:Shape and number, London: Macmillan : education. 1976, P.10

عبد الحميد لطفي، أحمد أبو العباس: تاريخ الرياضيات – القاهرة: المطبعة الأميركية، 1957، ص 7.

– عبد الحميد لطفي، المرجع السابق ذكره 29.

Joy, RR:Shape and number 1P11

Joy, RR:Shape and number

Joy, RR:Shape and number

– إبن النديم، محمد بن اسحق: الفهرست – بيروت: دار المعرفة، 1978، ص 28.

– عبد الله طحطاح: اسهام علماء الاسلام في الرياضيات. عالم الفكر(الكويت)، المجلد 11، العدد (1)، أبريل-يونيو 1980، ص 283-312 .

– عبد الحميد لطفي، المرجع السابق ذكره، ص 24 وحول إستخدام الأعداد أو الأرقام أنظر كذلك:

– دائرة المعارف الإسلامية، مادة الحساب.

– الأقليدس، أبو الحسن أحمد بن إبراهيم 341: الفصول في الحساب الهندي / تحقيق احمد سعيدان – عمان (الأردن): اللجنة الأردنية للتعريب والنشر والترجمة، 1973.

– ديتريش، البير: دور العرب في تطور العلوم الطبيعية. اللسان العربي (الرباط) العدد 2، يناير 1996، ص 96-105.

– موقع الأرقام : www.alargam.com